Glencoe

Algebra 2

Integration
Applications
Connections

Practice Masters

GLENCOE
McGraw-Hill

New York, New York   Columbus, Ohio   Woodland Hills, California   Peoria, Illnois

Glencoe/McGraw-Hill

*A Division of The **McGraw·Hill** Companies*

Send all inquiries to:
Glencoe/McGraw-Hill
8787 Orion Place
Columbus, Ohio 43240-4027

Algebra 2
Practice Masters

ISBN: 0-02-825148-2

6 7 8 9 10 024 03 02 01 00

Contents

NAME_____ DATE _____

Practice

Expressions and Formulas

Find the value of each expression.

1. $18 \div 2 \cdot 3$

2. $9 + 6 \div 2 + 1$

3. $(3 - 8)^2 \cdot 4 - 3$

4. $5 + 3 \cdot (2 - 12 \div 2)$

5. $1 + 2 - 3 \cdot 4 \div 5$

6. $12 - [20 - 2(6^2 \div 3 \cdot 2^2)]$

Evaluate each expression if $a = \frac{3}{4}$, $b = -8$, $c = -2$, $d = 3$, and $e = \frac{1}{3}$.

7. $ab^2 - d$

8. $(c + d)b$

9. $\dfrac{ae}{c} + d^2$

10. $\dfrac{d(b - c)}{ac}$

11. $(a - ce)c^2$

12. $a^2c^3 - be^2$

13. $-b[a + (c - d)^2]$

14. $\dfrac{a^3c^4}{d^3} - \dfrac{c}{e^2}$

Algebra 2

Practice

Expressions and Formulas

Find the value of each expression.

1. $18 \div 2 \cdot 3$ **27**

2. $9 + 6 \div 2 + 1$ **13**

3. $(3 - 8)^2 \cdot 4 - 3$ **97**

4. $5 + 3 \cdot (2 - 12 \div 2)$ **−7**

5. $1 + 2 - 3 \cdot 4 \div 5$ $\dfrac{3}{5}$

6. $12 - [20 - 2(6^2 \div 3 \cdot 2^2)]$ **88**

Evaluate each expression if $a = \dfrac{3}{4}$, $b = -8$, $c = -2$, $d = 3$, and $e = \dfrac{1}{3}$.

7. $ab^2 - d$ **45**

8. $(c + d)b$ **−8**

9. $\dfrac{ae}{c} + d^2$ $\dfrac{71}{8}$

10. $\dfrac{d(b - c)}{ac}$ **12**

11. $(a - ce)c^2$ $\dfrac{17}{3}$

12. $a^2c^3 - be^2$ $-\dfrac{65}{18}$

13. $-b[a + (c - d)^2]$ **206**

14. $\dfrac{a^3c^4}{d^3} - \dfrac{c}{e^2}$ $\dfrac{73}{4}$

NAME_____ DATE _____

Practice

Properties of Real Numbers

Name the sets of numbers to which each number belongs.

1. 6425

2. $\sqrt{7}$

3. π

4. 0

5. $\sqrt{\dfrac{25}{36}}$

6. $-\sqrt{16}$

7. -35

8. -31.8

Name the property illustrated by each equation.

9. $5x + (4y + 3x) = 5x + (3x + 4y)$

10. $7x + (9x + 8) = (7x + 9x) + 8$

11. $5(3x + y) = 5(3x + 1y)$

12. $7n + 2n = (7 + 2)n$

13. $3(2x)y = 3 \cdot 2(xy)$

14. $3x \cdot 2y = 3 \cdot 2 \cdot x \cdot y$

15. $(6 + -6)y = 0y$

16. $\dfrac{1}{4} \cdot 4y = 1y$

17. $5(x + y) = 5x + 5y$

18. $4n + 0 = 4n$

Simplify each expression.

19. $5x - 3y - 2x + 3y$

20. $-11a - 13b + 7a - 3b$

21. $8xy - 7y - (3 - 6y)$

22. $4c - 2c^2 - (4c + 2c^2)$

23. $3(r - 10s) - 4(7s + 2r)$

24. $\dfrac{1}{5}(10a - 4) + \dfrac{1}{2}(8 + 4a)$

25. $2x(4 - 2x + y) - 5x(y^2 + x - y)$

26. $\dfrac{5}{6}\left(\dfrac{3}{10}x + 12y\right) - \dfrac{1}{4}(2x - 3y)$

Algebra 2

NAME_____ DATE _____

Practice

Properties of Real Numbers

Name the sets of numbers to which each number belongs.

1. 6425
N, W, Z, Q, R

2. $\sqrt{7}$ **I, R**

3. π **I, R**

4. 0 **W, Z, Q, R**

5. $\sqrt{\dfrac{25}{36}}$ **Q, R**

6. $-\sqrt{16}$ **Z, Q, R**

7. -35 **Z, Q, R**

8. -31.8 **Q, R**

Name the property illustrated by each equation.

9. $5x + (4y + 3x) = 5x + (3x + 4y)$
commutative +

10. $7x + (9x + 8) = (7x + 9x) + 8$
associative +

11. $5(3x + y) = 5(3x + 1y)$ **identity $\times$**

12. $7n + 2n = (7 + 2)n$ **distributive**

13. $3(2x)y = 3 \cdot 2(xy)$ **associative $\times$**

14. $3x \cdot 2y = 3 \cdot 2 \cdot x \cdot y$ **commutative $\times$**

15. $(6 + -6)y = 0y$ **inverse +**

16. $\dfrac{1}{4} \cdot 4y = 1y$ **inverse $\times$**

17. $5(x + y) = 5x + 5y$ **distributive**

18. $4n + 0 = 4n$ **identity +**

Simplify each expression.

19. $5x - 3y - 2x + 3y$ **3x**

20. $-11a - 13b + 7a - 3b$ **$-4a - 16b$**

21. $8xy - 7y - (3 - 6y)$ **$8xy - y - 3$**

22. $4c - 2c^2 - (4c + 2c^2)$ **$-4c^2$**

23. $3(r - 10s) - 4(7s + 2r)$
$-5r - 58s$

24. $\dfrac{1}{5}(10a - 4) + \dfrac{1}{2}(8 + 4a)$ **$4a + \dfrac{16}{5}$**

25. $2x(4 - 2x + y) - 5x(y^2 + x - y)$
$-5xy^2 + 7xy - 9x^2 + 8x$

26. $\dfrac{5}{6}\left(\dfrac{3}{10}x + 12y\right) - \dfrac{1}{4}(2x - 3y)$
$\dfrac{-x + 43y}{4}$

Practice

Integration: Statistics
Graphs and Measures of Central Tendency

The following tables give the number of games bowled and total points scored for two bowling teams for the season.

Pin Struck		
Player	No. of games	Points
Bob	111	17,316
Cindy	93	11,625
Steve	87	11,832
Cheri	110	15,070
Juan	108	19,008

Bowl Downers		
Player	No. of games	Points
Kiko	96	10,752
Paul	84	12,348
Clarice	111	14,319
Bethany	105	10,290
Jarrod	99	16,731

1. Make a stem-and-leaf plot of the number of games bowled by the 10 players.

2. Who had the highest total points?

3. Who had the lowest total points?

4. Find the mode of the number of games played.

Each number below represents the weight of a person in Mr. Miller's math class.

134 116 146 152 124 110 137 108 110 132
 98 221   86 143 114 104 121 127 137 110

5. Make a line plot of the weights of the people in the class.

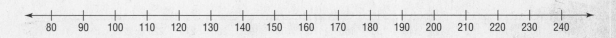

6. What is the weight of the heaviest person?

7. Which weight(s) occur most frequently?

8. Find the median of the data.

9. Find the mean of the data.

Algebra 2

NAME _____ DATE _____

Practice

Integration: Statistics
Graphs and Measures of Central Tendency

The following tables give the number of games bowled and total points scored for two bowling teams for the season.

Pin Struck		
Player	No. of games	Points
Bob	111	17,316
Cindy	93	11,625
Steve	87	11,832
Cheri	110	15,070
Juan	108	19,008

Bowl Downers		
Player	No. of games	Points
Kiko	96	10,752
Paul	84	12,348
Clarice	111	14,319
Bethany	105	10,290
Jarrod	99	16,731

1. Make a stem-and-leaf plot of the number of games bowled by the 10 players.

Stem	Leaf
8	4 7
9	3 6 9
10	5 8
11	0 1 1

2. Who had the highest total points? **Juan**

3. Who had the lowest total points? **Bethany**

4. Find the mode of the number of games played. **111**

Each number below represents the weight of a person in Mr. Miller's math class.

134   116   146   152   124   110   137   108   110   132
98   221   86   143   114   104   121   127   137   110

5. Make a line plot of the weights of the people in the class.

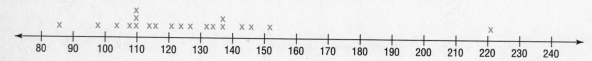

6. What is the weight of the heaviest person? **221**

7. Which weight(s) occur most frequently? **110**

8. Find the median of the data. **122.5**

9. Find the mean of the data. **126.5**

     Algebra 2

NAME_____ DATE _____

Practice

Solving Equations

Solve each equation.

1. $13 = 8 - 6r$

2. $9 + 4n = -59$

3. $\frac{3}{8}y = 2\frac{3}{4}$

4. $-6 = \frac{4x}{7} + 2$

5. $\frac{3}{4} - \frac{1}{2}n = \frac{4}{5}$

6. $\frac{5}{6}s + \frac{3}{8} = \frac{2}{3}$

7. $-1.6r + 5 = -7.8$

8. $6x - 5 = 7 - 9x$

9. $5(6 - 4v) = v + 21$

10. $-4(6y - 5) = 23 - 3(8y + 1)$

Define a variable, write an equation, and solve the problem.

11. Fourteen less than twice some number is 154. Find the number.

12. The length of a rectangle is 9 centimeters more than half the width. Find the length if the perimeter is 60 centimeters.

13. In an evening, a sporting goods store sold twice as many T-shirts as shorts. T-shirts are $9 each, and shorts are $14 each. The total amount of money taken in for both items was $256. Find the number of each that was sold.

Algebra 2

Solving Equations

Solve each equation.

1. $13 = 8 - 6r$ $-\dfrac{5}{6}$

2. $9 + 4n = -59$ -17

3. $\dfrac{3}{8}y = 2\dfrac{3}{4}$ $\dfrac{22}{3}$

4. $-6 = \dfrac{4x}{7} + 2$ -14

5. $\dfrac{3}{4} - \dfrac{1}{2}n = \dfrac{4}{5}$ $-\dfrac{1}{10}$

6. $\dfrac{5}{6}s + \dfrac{3}{8} = \dfrac{2}{3}$ $\dfrac{7}{20}$

7. $-1.6r + 5 = -7.8$ **8**

8. $6x - 5 = 7 - 9x$ $\dfrac{4}{5}$

9. $5(6 - 4v) = v + 21$ $\dfrac{3}{7}$

10. $-4(6y - 5) = 23 - 3(8y + 1)$
all reals

Define a variable, write an equation, and solve the problem.

11. Fourteen less than twice some number is 154. Find the number. **84**

12. The length of a rectangle is 9 centimeters more than half the width. Find the length if the perimeter is 60 centimeters.
16 cm

13. In an evening, a sporting goods store sold twice as many T-shirts as shorts. T-shirts are $9 each, and shorts are $14 each. The total amount of money taken in for both items was $256. Find the number of each that was sold.
8 shorts, 16 T-shirts

NAME_____ DATE _____

Practice

Solving Absolute Value Equations

Solve each equation.

1. $|n - 4| = 13$

2. $7|x + 3| = 42$

3. $|2y - 3| = 29$

4. $\left|x - \frac{3}{8}\right| = 2$

5. $\left|\frac{2}{3}u - 6\right| = 42$

6. $|5x - 4| = -6$

7. $-3|4x - 9| = 24$

8. $-6|5 - 2y| = -9$

9. $|8 + p| = 2p - 3$

10. $5|4w - 1| = 5w + 40$

11. $4|2y - 7| + 5 = 9$

12. $-2|7 - 3y| - 6 = -14$

List possibilities to answer each problem.

13. In how many ways can a clerk give a customer 25¢ in change?

14. In how many ways can you select three different numbers from the set {1, 2, 3, 4, 5, 6, 7, 8} so that the numbers could represent the measures of the sides of a triangle? Remember that the sum of the measures of any two sides of a triangle must be greater than the measure of the other side.

Algebra 2

1-5

Practice

Solving Absolute Value Equations

Solve each equation.

1. $|n - 4| = 13$ $-9, 17$

2. $7|x + 3| = 42$ $-9, 3$

3. $|2y - 3| = 29$ $-13, 16$

4. $\left|x - \dfrac{3}{8}\right| = 2$ $-\dfrac{13}{8}, \dfrac{19}{8}$

5. $\left|\dfrac{2}{3}u - 6\right| = 42$ $-54, 72$

6. $|5x - 4| = -6$ **no solution**

7. $-3|4x - 9| = 24$ **no solution**

8. $-6|5 - 2y| = -9$ $\dfrac{7}{4}, \dfrac{13}{4}$

9. $|8 + p| = 2p - 3$ **11**

10. $5|4w - 1| = 5w + 40$ $-\dfrac{7}{5}, 3$

11. $4|2y - 7| + 5 = 9$ **3, 4**

12. $-2|7 - 3y| - 6 = -14$ $1, \dfrac{11}{3}$

List possibilities to answer each problem.

13. In how many ways can a clerk give a customer 25¢ in change?   **13 ways**

14. In how many ways can you select three different numbers from the set {1, 2, 3, 4, 5, 6, 7, 8} so that the numbers could represent the measures of the sides of a triangle? Remember that the sum of the measures of any two sides of a triangle must be greater than the measure of the other side.
22 ways

Practice

Solving Inequalities

Solve each inequality. Graph the solution set.

1. $8x - 6 \geq 10$

2. $23 - 4u < 3$

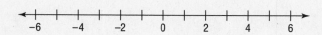

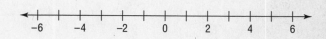

3. $-3(4w - 1) > -12$

4. $5(2x + 3) \leq 4$

Solve each inequality.

5. $9x - 11 > 4x + 12$

6. $1 - 8u \leq 3u - 10$

7. $16 - 10r \geq 0$

8. $9(2r - 5) - 3 < 7r - 4$

9. $1 + 5(x - 8) \leq 2 - (x + 5)$

10. $4n - 5(n - 3) > 3(n + 1) - 20$

11. $17.5 < 19 - 2.5x$

12. $\dfrac{5x}{8} - \dfrac{3}{4} < \dfrac{1}{5}$

13. $-6\left(\dfrac{1}{2} + \dfrac{2w}{3}\right) > 2w$

14. $\dfrac{4x - 3}{2} \geq -1.9$

Solving Inequalities

Solve each inequality. Graph the solution set.

1. $8x - 6 \geq 10$ $\{x|x \geq 2\}$

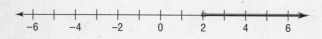

2. $23 - 4u < 3$ $\{u|u > 5\}$

3. $-3(4w - 1) > -12$ $\left\{w|w < \dfrac{5}{4}\right\}$

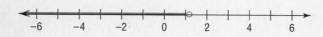

4. $5(2x + 3) \leq 4$ $\left\{x|x \leq -\dfrac{11}{10}\right\}$

Solve each inequality.

5. $9x - 11 > 4x + 12$ $\left\{x|x > \dfrac{23}{5}\right\}$

6. $1 - 8u \leq 3u - 10$ $\{u|u \geq 1\}$

7. $16 - 10r \geq 0$ $\left\{r|r \leq \dfrac{8}{5}\right\}$

8. $9(2r - 5) - 3 < 7r - 4$ $\{r|r < 4\}$

9. $1 + 5(x - 8) \leq 2 - (x + 5)$ $\{x|x \leq 6\}$

10. $4n - 5(n - 3) > 3(n + 1) - 20$
$\{n|n < 8\}$

11. $17.5 < 19 - 2.5x$ $\{x|x < 0.6\}$

12. $\dfrac{5x}{8} - \dfrac{3}{4} < \dfrac{1}{5}$ $\left\{x|x < \dfrac{38}{25}\right\}$

13. $-6\left(\dfrac{1}{2} + \dfrac{2w}{3}\right) > 2w$ $\left\{w|w < -\dfrac{1}{2}\right\}$

14. $\dfrac{4x - 3}{2} \geq -1.9$ $\{x|x \geq -0.2\}$

Solving Absolute Value Inequalities

Solve each inequality. Graph each solution set.

1. $-8 \leq 3y - 20 < 52$

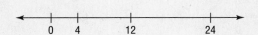

2. $3(5x - 2) < 24$ or $6x - 4 > 9 + 5x$

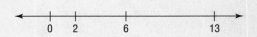

3. $2x - 3 > 15$ or $3 - 7x < 17$

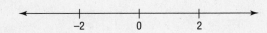

4. $35 - 5x \leq 0$ and $5x + 6 \geq -14$

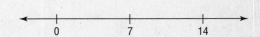

5. $|2w| \geq 5$

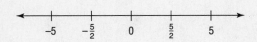

6. $|y + 5| < 2$

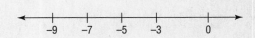

7. $|x - 8| \geq 3$

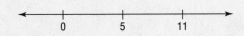

8. $|3x - 2| \leq -2$

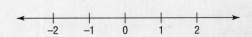

9. $|x + 2| \leq 2x + 7$

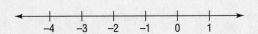

10. $|x| > x - 1$

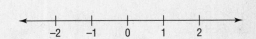

Solving Absolute Value Inequalities

Solve each inequality. Graph each solution set.

1. $-8 \leq 3y - 20 < 52$
$\{y|4 \leq y < 24\}$

2. $3(5x - 2) < 24$ or $6x - 4 > 9 + 5x$
$\{x|x < 2 \text{ or } x > 13\}$

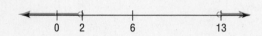

3. $2x - 3 > 15$ or $3 - 7x < 17$
$\{x|x > -2\}$

4. $35 - 5x \leq 0$ and $5x + 6 \geq -14$
$\{x|x \geq 7\}$

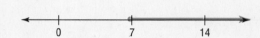

5. $|2w| \geq 5$
$\left\{w|w \leq -\dfrac{5}{2} \text{ or } w \geq \dfrac{5}{2}\right\}$

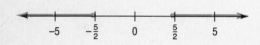

6. $|y + 5| < 2$
$\{y| -7 < y < -3\}$

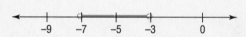

7. $|x - 8| \geq 3$
$\{x|x \leq 5 \text{ or } x \geq 11\}$

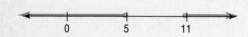

8. $|3x - 2| \leq -2$
$\emptyset$

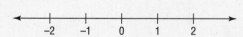

9. $|x + 2| \leq 2x + 7$
$\{x|x \geq -3\}$

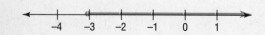

10. $|x| > x - 1$
all reals

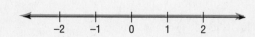

Relations and Functions

State the domain and range of each relation. Then graph and identify whether it is a function or not. For each function, state whether it is discrete or continuous.

1. {(0.75, 0.5), (0.75, −0.5), (−0.75, 0.5)}

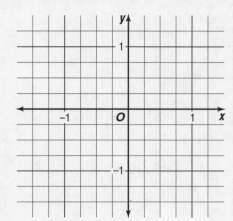

2. {(−20, −7), (20, 0), (0, 15), (10, 0)}

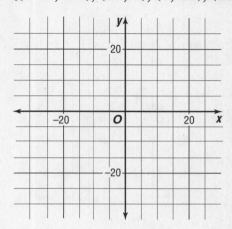

State the domain and range of each relation. Is the relation a function?

3. {(3, 2), (3, 5), (3, 8)}

4. {(2, 6), (6, 2)}

Use the vertical line test to determine if each relation is a function.

5.

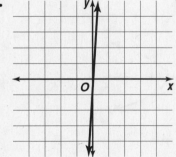

6.

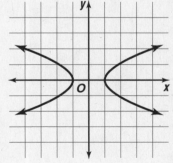

Find each value if f(x) = $\dfrac{5}{x + 2}$.

7. $f(3)$

8. $f(-4)$

9. $f\left(\dfrac{1}{2}\right)$

10. $f(-2)$

11. $f(0)$

12. $f(m - 2)$

NAME_____ DATE _____

Practice

Relations and Functions

State the domain and range of each relation. Then graph and identify whether it is a function or not. For each function, state whether it is discrete or continuous.

1. {(0.75, 0.5), (0.75, −0.5), (−0.75, 0.5)}   **2.** {(−20, −7), (20, 0), (0, 15), (10, 0)}

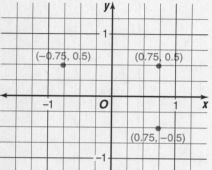

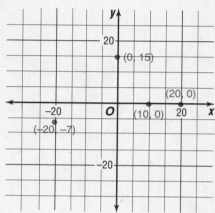

d: {0.75, −0.75}, *r*: {−0.5, 0.5}; not a function

d: {−20, 0, 10, 20}, *r*: {−7, 0, 15}; function; discrete

State the domain and range of each relation. Is the relation a function?

3. {(3, 2), (3, 5), (3, 8)} *d*: {3}, *r*: {2, 5, 8}; not a function

4. {(2, 6), (6, 2)} *d*: {2, 6}, *r*: {2, 6}; function

Use the vertical line test to determine if each relation is a function.

5. 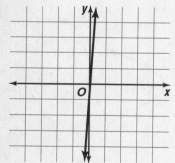   function

6. 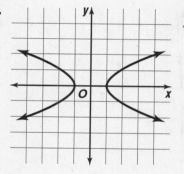   not a function

Find each value if $f(x) = \dfrac{5}{x+2}$.

7. $f(3)$ **1**

8. $f(-4)$ $-\dfrac{5}{2}$

9. $f\left(\dfrac{1}{2}\right)$ **2**

10. $f(-2)$ **undefined**

11. $f(0)$ $\dfrac{5}{2}$

12. $f(m-2)$ $\dfrac{5}{m}$

     Algebra 2

Practice

Linear Equations

Write each equation in standard form.

1. $y = 7x - 5$

2. $y = \dfrac{3}{8}x + 5$

3. $x = -\dfrac{2}{7}y + \dfrac{3}{4}$

4. $3y - 5 = 0$

Find the x-intercept and y-intercept of the graph of each equation.

5. $2x - y = 5$

6. $3x = 4y - 5$

7. $3x - 6 = y$

8. $5x + 2y = 6$

Graph each equation.

9. $y = 3x - 1$

10. $f(x) = -2x + 3$

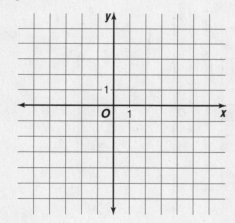

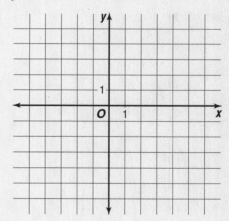

11. $2x + 7y = 14$

12. $\dfrac{2}{5}x + \dfrac{y}{4} = 1$

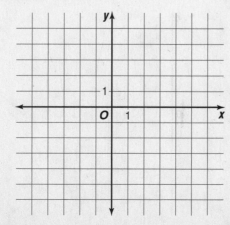

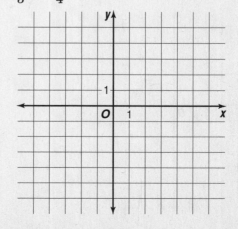

Practice

Linear Equations

Write each equation in standard form.

1. $y = 7x - 5$
$7x - y = 5$

2. $y = \frac{3}{8}x + 5$
$3x - 8y = -40$

3. $x = -\frac{2}{7}y + \frac{3}{4}$
$28x + 8y = 21$

4. $3y - 5 = 0$
$3y = 5$

Find the x-intercept and y-intercept of the graph of each equation.

5. $2x - y = 5$
x-intercept: $\frac{5}{2}$; y-intercept: -5

6. $3x = 4y - 5$
x-intercept: $-\frac{5}{3}$; y-intercept: $\frac{5}{4}$

7. $3x - 6 = y$
x-intercept: 2; y-intercept: -6

8. $5x + 2y = 6$
x-intercept: $\frac{6}{5}$; y-intercept: 3

Graph each equation.

9. $y = 3x - 1$

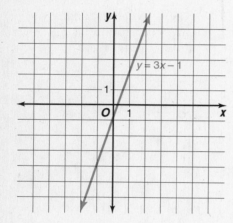

10. $f(x) = -2x + 3$

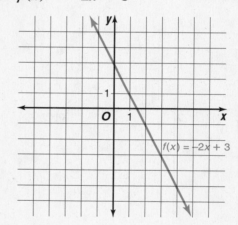

11. $2x + 7y = 14$

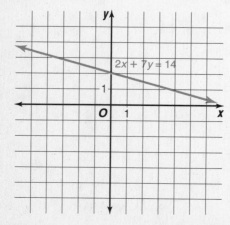

12. $\frac{2}{5}x + \frac{y}{4} = 1$

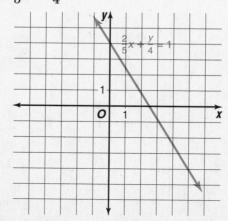

Practice

Slope

Find the slope of the line that passes through each pair of points.

1. $(3, -8)$ and $(-5, 2)$

2. $(-10, -3)$ and $(7, 2)$

3. $(-7, -6)$ and $(3, -6)$

4. $(8, 2)$ and $(8, -1)$

Graph a line that passes through the given point and has the given slope.

5. $(1, -3)$, $m = 3$

6. $(2, 1)$, $m = -\dfrac{3}{4}$

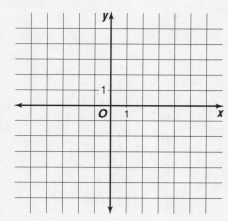

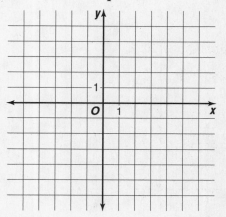

State whether the graphs of the following equations are parallel, perpendicular, or neither.

7. $2x + 3y = 4$
$3x + 2y = 6$

8. $\dfrac{1}{2}x + 2y = 1$
$4x - y = 3$

9. $6x - 9y = 4$
$\dfrac{2}{3}x - y = 11$

10. $y - 7 = 0$
$3x = 5$

11. Look for a Pattern A pyramid of aluminum cans is built against a wall so that there are two cans in the top row, four cans in the second row, six cans in the third row, and so on. How many rows are there if the pyramid contains 1190 cans?

Algebra 2

Slope

Find the slope of the line that passes through each pair of points.

1. $(3, -8)$ and $(-5, 2)$ $\quad -\dfrac{5}{4}$

2. $(-10, -3)$ and $(7, 2)$ $\quad \dfrac{5}{17}$

3. $(-7, -6)$ and $(3, -6)$ **0**

4. $(8, 2)$ and $(8, -1)$ **undefined**

Graph a line that passes through the given point and has the given slope.

5. $(1, -3)$, $m = 3$

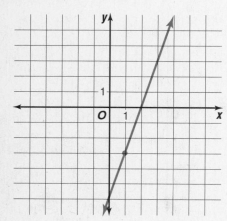

6. $(2, 1)$, $m = -\dfrac{3}{4}$

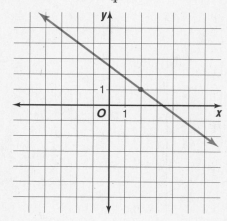

State whether the graphs of the following equations are parallel, perpendicular, or neither.

7. $2x + 3y = 4$
$3x + 2y = 6$
neither

8. $\dfrac{1}{2}x + 2y = 1$
$4x - y = 3$
perpendicular

9. $6x - 9y = 4$
$\dfrac{2}{3}x - y = 11$
parallel

10. $y - 7 = 0$
$3x = 5$
perpendicular

11. Look for a Pattern A pyramid of aluminum cans is built against a wall so that there are two cans in the top row, four cans in the second row, six cans in the third row, and so on. How many rows are there if the pyramid contains 1190 cans? **34**

NAME_____ DATE _____

Practice

Writing Linear Equations

State the slope and y-intercept of the graph of each equation.

1. $5x - 4y = 8$

2. $3x - y = -11$

3. $\frac{2}{3}x + \frac{4}{7}y = 1$

4. $3y = 7$

Write each equation in slope-intercept form.

5. $3x - 5y = 15$

6. $4x + 7y = 12$

7. $7y = -15$

8. $2x = -8$

Write an equation in slope-intercept form that satisfies each given condition.

9. slope $= -5$, passes through $(-3, -8)$

10. slope $= \frac{4}{5}$, passes through $(10, -3)$

11. passes through $(4, 3)$ and $(7, -2)$

12. passes through $(-6, -3)$ and $(-8, 4)$

13. passes through $(3, 11)$ and $(-6, 5)$

14. passes through $(7, 2)$ and $(3, -5)$

15. x-intercept $= 3$, y-intercept $= 2$

16. x-intercept $= -5$, y-intercept $= 7$

17. x-intercept $= -5$, y-intercept $= -5$

18. x-intercept $= \frac{1}{2}$, y-intercept $= 4$

Practice

Writing Linear Equations

State the slope and y-intercept of the graph of each equation.

1. $5x - 4y = 8$ $\quad m = \frac{5}{4}, b = -2$

2. $3x - y = -11$ $\quad m = 3, b = 11$

3. $\frac{2}{3}x + \frac{4}{7}y = 1$ $\quad m = -\frac{7}{6}, b = \frac{7}{4}$

4. $3y = 7$ $\quad m = 0, b = \frac{7}{3}$

Write each equation in slope-intercept form.

5. $3x - 5y = 15$ $\quad y = \frac{3}{5}x - 3$

6. $4x + 7y = 12$ $\quad y = -\frac{4}{7}x + \frac{12}{7}$

7. $7y = -15$ $\quad y = -\frac{15}{7}$

8. $2x = -8$ **no slope-intercept form**

Write an equation in slope-intercept form that satisfies each given condition.

9. slope $= -5$, passes through $(-3, -8)$
$y = -5x - 23$

10. slope $= \frac{4}{5}$, passes through $(10, -3)$
$y = \frac{4}{5}x - 11$

11. passes through $(4, 3)$ and $(7, -2)$
$y = -\frac{5}{3}x + \frac{29}{3}$

12. passes through $(-6, -3)$ and $(-8, 4)$
$y = -\frac{7}{2}x - 24$

13. passes through $(3, 11)$ and $(-6, 5)$
$y = \frac{2}{3}x + 9$

14. passes through $(7, 2)$ and $(3, -5)$
$y = \frac{7}{4}x - \frac{41}{4}$

15. x-intercept $= 3$, y-intercept $= 2$
$y = -\frac{2}{3}x + 2$

16. x-intercept $= -5$, y-intercept $= 7$
$y = \frac{7}{5}x + 7$

17. x-intercept $= -5$, y-intercept $= -5$
$y = -x - 5$

18. x-intercept $= \frac{1}{2}$, y-intercept $= 4$
$y = -8x + 4$

NAME_____ DATE _____

Practice

Integration: Statistics
Modeling Real-World Data Using Scatter Plots

According to a certain linear prediction equation, a person 25 years old needs 2400 calories of food intake a day. A person 30 years old needs 2300 calories. Let x stand for age in years and y stand for calories.

1. Find the slope of the prediction equation.

2. Find the y-intercept of the prediction equation. What does it measure?

3. Write the prediction equation.

4. Predict the caloric needs of a person who is 34 years old.

The Cody Company ran a study on its sales force and learned that the average number of years of experience for each sales team was in direct relation to annual sales volume. Use the data below to answer the following.

Annual Sales (in thousands)	46	35	51	42	33	50	30
Average Years of Experience	6	4	8	5.5	3	7	2.5

5. Draw a scatter plot to show how years of experience per sales team and annual sales are related.

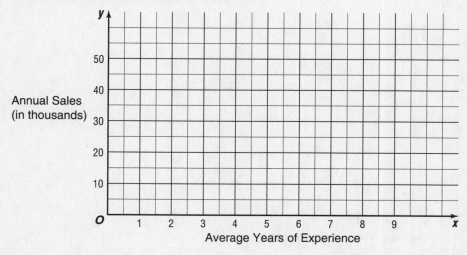

6. Find a prediction equation to show how years of experience and annual sales are related.

Integration: Statistics
Modeling Real-World Data Using Scatter Plots

According to a certain linear prediction equation, a person 25 years old needs 2400 calories of food intake a day. A person 30 years old needs 2300 calories. Let x stand for age in years and y stand for calories.

1. Find the slope of the prediction equation. -20

2. Find the y-intercept of the prediction equation. What does it measure? 2900; the calories needed by a newborn

3. Write the prediction equation. $y = -20x + 2900$

4. Predict the caloric needs of a person who is 34 years old. 2220 calories

The Cody Company ran a study on its sales force and learned that the average number of years of experience for each sales team was in direct relation to annual sales volume. Use the data below to answer the following.

Annual Sales (in thousands)	46	35	51	42	33	50	30
Average Years of Experience	6	4	8	5.5	3	7	2.5

5. Draw a scatter plot to show how years of experience per sales team and annual sales are related.

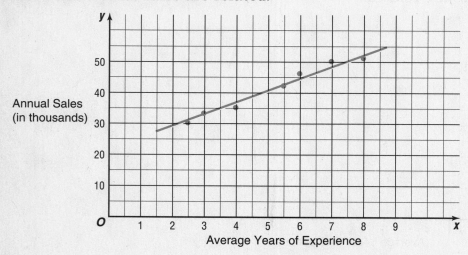

6. Find a prediction equation to show how years of experience and annual sales are related. Typical answer: $y = 3.6x + 22.2$

NAME_____ DATE _____

Practice

Special Functions

If $g(x) = |-3x + 1|$ and $h(x) = \left[\frac{1}{2}x\right]$, find each value.

1. $g\left(\frac{1}{3}\right)$ **2.** $h\left(\frac{1}{3}\right)$ **3.** $g(-7)$ **4.** $h(-7)$

Graph each function.

5. $y = |-3x|$

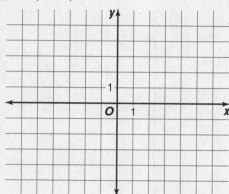

6. $y + 2 = |x + 1|$

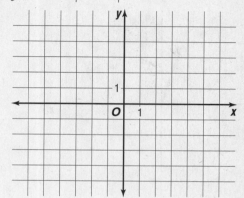

7. $y = |3x - 6|$

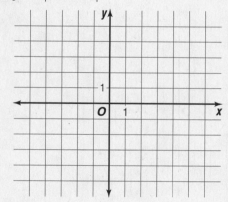

8. $y = [-5x]$

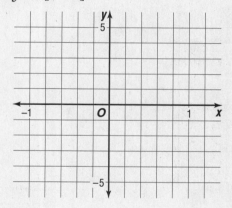

9. $y - 2 = [x + 3]$

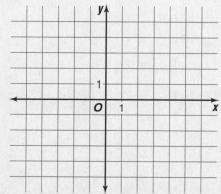

10. $y = [2x - 1]$

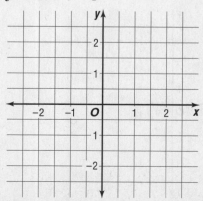

Algebra 2

Special Functions

If g(x) = |−3x + 1| and h(x) = $\left[\frac{1}{2}x\right]$, find each value.

1. $g\left(\frac{1}{3}\right)$ **0**

2. $h\left(\frac{1}{3}\right)$ **0**

3. $g(-7)$ **22**

4. $h(-7)$ **−4**

Graph each function.

5. $y = |-3x|$

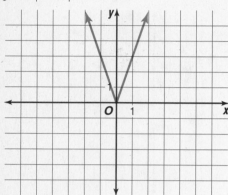

6. $y + 2 = |x + 1|$

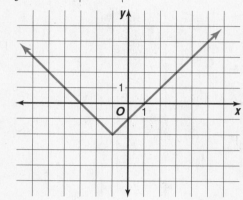

7. $y = |3x - 6|$

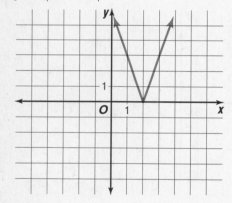

8. $y = [-5x]$

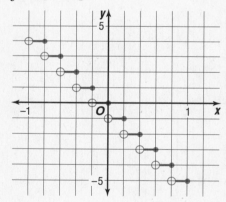

9. $y - 2 = [x + 3]$

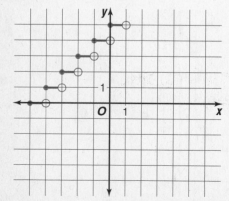

10. $y = [2x - 1]$

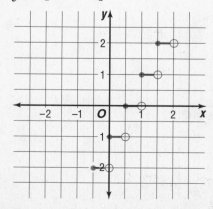

Algebra 2

NAME_____ DATE _____

Practice

Student Edition
Pages 110–114

Linear Inequalities

Graph each inequality.

1. $3 - x > 0$

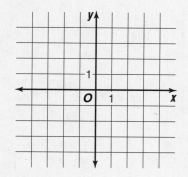

2. $y < -4x - 2$

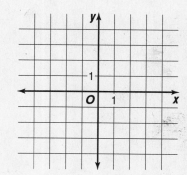

3. $y \geq 2x + 5$

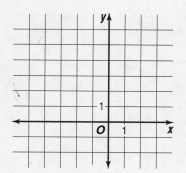

4. $x - 3y \leq 6$

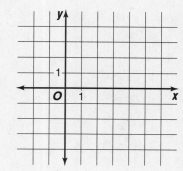

5. $y > |x| - 1$

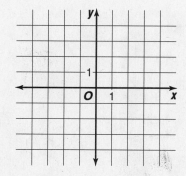

6. $y > -3|x + 1| - 2$

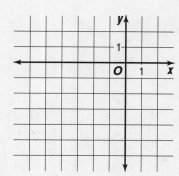

2-7

Practice

Linear Inequalities

Graph each inequality.

1. $3 - x > 0$

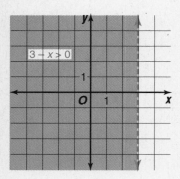

2. $y < -4x - 2$

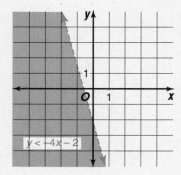

3. $y \geq 2x + 5$

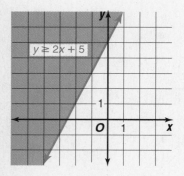

4. $x - 3y \leq 6$

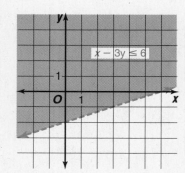

5. $y > |x| - 1$

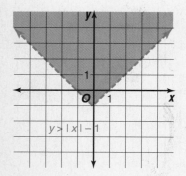

6. $y > -3|x + 1| - 2$

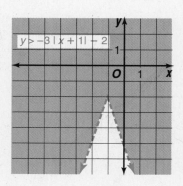

Algebra 2

NAME_____ DATE _____

Practice

Graphing Systems of Equations

Graph each system of equations and state its solution. Also, state whether the system is consistent and independent, consistent and dependent, or inconsistent.

1. $2x + y = 4$
$x - y = 2$

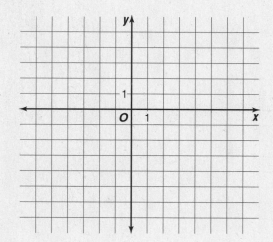

2. $x + y = 2$
$x + y = 6$

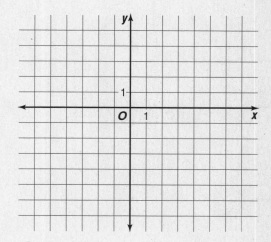

3. $2y - 8 = x$
$y = \frac{1}{2}x + 4$

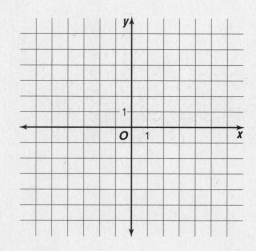

4. $x - 2y = 0$
$y = 2x - 3$

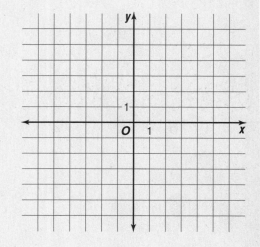

Algebra 2

Graphing Systems of Equations

Graph each system of equations and state its solution. Also,
state whether the system is consistent and independent,
consistent and dependent, or inconsistent.

1. $2x + y = 4$ (2, 0); consistent
   $x - y = 2$ and independent

2. $x + y = 2$ no solutions;
   $x + y = 6$ inconsistent

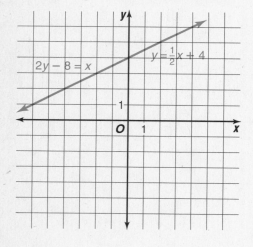

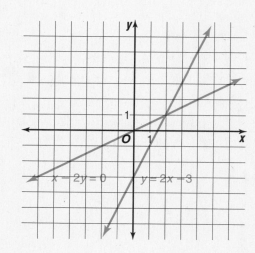

3. $2y - 8 = x$ all points on the
   $y = \frac{1}{2}x + 4$ line; consistent
   and dependent

4. $x - 2y = 0$ (2, 1); consistent
   $y = 2x - 3$ and independent

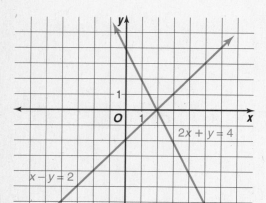

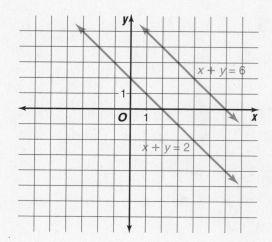

NAME_____ DATE _____

Practice

Solving Systems of Equations Algebraically

Solve each system of equations by using substitution.

1. $2x + y = 4$
$3x + 2y = 1$

2. $x - 9 = 3y$
$x + 2y = -1$

3. $x + 3y = 8$
$\frac{1}{3}x + y = 9$

4. $2x - 3y = 6$
$-\frac{2}{3}x + y = -2$

Solve each system of equations by using elimination.

5. $2x + y = 1$
$3x - y = 14$

6. $2x - y = -1$
$3x + 2y = 30$

7. $6x + 3y = 6$
$8x + 5y = 12$

8. $\frac{3x - y}{2} = 5$
$\frac{4x - y}{4} = 4$

Solve each system of equations. Use either substitution or elimination.

9. $8x + 3y + 5 = 0$
$10x + 6y + 13 = 0$

10. $\frac{2x}{5} - \frac{3y}{4} = -2$
$\frac{x}{2} + \frac{y}{4} = 7$

11. $\frac{x}{4} - \frac{y}{3} = 1$
$\frac{1}{3}x - \frac{4y}{9} = \frac{4}{3}$

12. $4x - 2y = 5$
$2x = y - 1$

Solving Systems of Equations Algebraically

Solve each system of equations by using substitution.

1. $2x + y = 4$
   $3x + 2y = 1$ **(7, −10)**

2. $x - 9 = 3y$
   $x + 2y = -1$ **(3, −2)**

3. $x + 3y = 8$
   $\frac{1}{3}x + y = 9$ **no solutions**

4. $2x - 3y = 6$
   $-\frac{2}{3}x + y = -2$
   {(x, y)|2x − 3y = 6}

Solve each system of equations by using elimination.

5. $2x + y = 1$
   $3x - y = 14$ **(3, −5)**

6. $2x - y = -1$
   $3x + 2y = 30$ **(4, 9)**

7. $6x + 3y = 6$
   $8x + 5y = 12$ **(−1, 4)**

8. $\frac{3x - y}{2} = 5$
   $\frac{4x - y}{4} = 4$ **(6, 8)**

Solve each system of equations. Use either substitution or elimination.

9. $8x + 3y + 5 = 0$
   $10x + 6y + 13 = 0$ $\left(\frac{1}{2}, -3\right)$

10. $\frac{2x}{5} - \frac{3y}{4} = -2$
    $\frac{x}{2} + \frac{y}{4} = 7$ **(10, 8)**

11. $\frac{x}{4} - \frac{y}{3} = 1$
    $\frac{1}{3}x - \frac{4y}{9} = \frac{4}{3}$ $\left\{(x, y) \,\middle|\, \frac{x}{4} - \frac{y}{3} = 1\right\}$

12. $4x - 2y = 5$
    $2x = y - 1$ **no solutions**

Practice

Cramer's Rule

Find the value of each determinant.

1. $\begin{vmatrix} 3 & 8 \\ 4 & 5 \end{vmatrix}$

2. $\begin{vmatrix} -6 & 5 \\ -4 & 9 \end{vmatrix}$

3. $\begin{vmatrix} -7 & -3 \\ -2 & -6 \end{vmatrix}$

4. $\begin{vmatrix} 5 & 10 \\ -6 & 8 \end{vmatrix}$

Use Cramer's rule to solve each system of equations.

5. $4x - 3y = -6$
$x + 2y = -7$

6. $5s + 6u = 1$
$-2s - u = -6$

7. $2w - 5z = 13$
$6w + 3z = 10$

8. $m + 3p = -6$
$2m - 5p = 7$

9. $2x - 4y = 1$
$-x + 2y = 5$

10. $3c + 9d = 2$
$c + 3d = \dfrac{2}{3}$

Practice

Cramer's Rule

Find the value of each determinant.

1. $\begin{vmatrix} 3 & 8 \\ 4 & 5 \end{vmatrix}$ -17

2. $\begin{vmatrix} -6 & 5 \\ -4 & 9 \end{vmatrix}$ -34

3. $\begin{vmatrix} -7 & -3 \\ -2 & -6 \end{vmatrix}$ 36

4. $\begin{vmatrix} 5 & 10 \\ -6 & 8 \end{vmatrix}$ 100

Use Cramer's rule to solve each system of equations.

5. $4x - 3y = -6$
   $x + 2y = -7$ $(-3, -2)$

6. $5s + 6u = 1$
   $-2s - u = -6$ $(5, -4)$

7. $2w - 5z = 13$
   $6w + 3z = 10$ $\left(\dfrac{89}{36}, -\dfrac{29}{18}\right)$

8. $m + 3p = -6$
   $2m - 5p = 7$ $\left(-\dfrac{9}{11}, -\dfrac{19}{11}\right)$

9. $2x - 4y = 1$
   $-x + 2y = 5$ **no solutions**

10. $3c + 9d = 2$
    $c + 3d = \dfrac{2}{3}$ $\{(c, d)|3c + 9d = 2\}$

Practice

Graphing Systems of Inequalities

Solve each system of inequalities by graphing.

1. $y + 1 < -x$
   $y \geq 1$

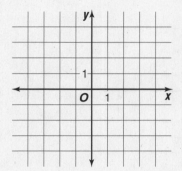

2. $x > -2$
   $2y \geq 3x + 6$

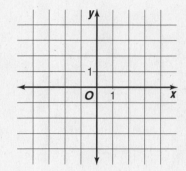

3. $y \leq 2x - 3$
   $y \leq -\frac{1}{2}x + 2$

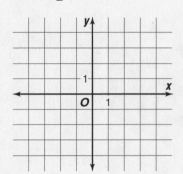

4. $y > -x - 2$
   $y \leq 3x + 2$

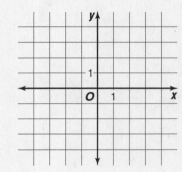

5. $|y| \leq 1$
   $y \leq |x| - 1$

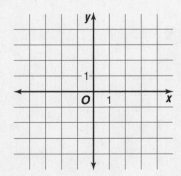

6. $x > -1$
   $y < \frac{2}{3}x + 2$
   $3y > 4x$

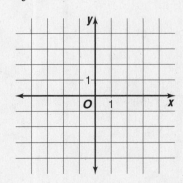

3-4

Practice

Graphing Systems of Inequalities

Solve each system of inequalities by graphing.

1. $y + 1 < -x$
$\quad y \geq 1$

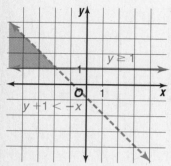

2. $x > -2$
$\quad 2y \geq 3x + 6$

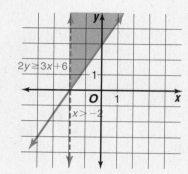

3. $y \leq 2x - 3$
$\quad y \leq -\frac{1}{2}x + 2$

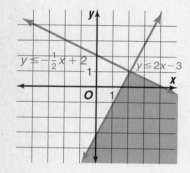

4. $y > -x - 2$
$\quad y \leq 3x + 2$

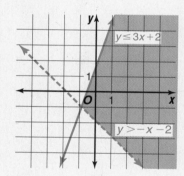

5. $|y| \leq 1$
$\quad y \leq |x| - 1$

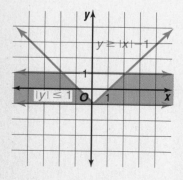

6. $x > -1$
$\quad y < \frac{2}{3}x + 2$
$\quad 3y > 4x$

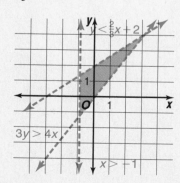

Algebra 2

Linear Programming

Graph each system of inequalities. Name the coordinates of the vertices of the feasible region. Find the maximum and minimum values of the given function for this region.

1. $2x - 4 \leq y$
$-2x - 4 \leq y$
$2 \geq y$
$f(x, y) = -2x + y$

2. $3x - y \leq 7$
$2x - y \geq 3$
$y \geq x - 3$
$f(x, y) = x - 4y$

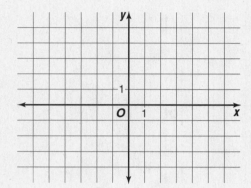
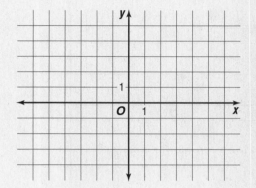

3. $x \geq 0$
$y \geq 0$
$3x + y \leq 15$
$y \leq 6$
$f(x, y) = 3x + y$

4. $x \leq 0$
$y \leq 0$
$4x + y \geq -7$
$f(x, y) = -x - 4y$

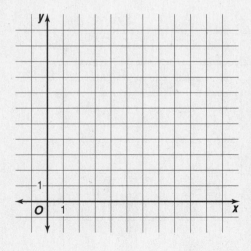
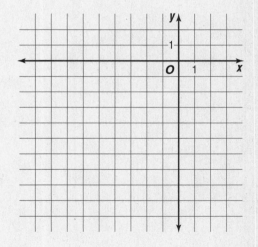

5. Solve a simpler problem. A snail is at the bottom of a well that is 24 feet deep. The snail can climb 2 inches each hour, but then falls back 1 inch. How many hours will it take the snail to crawl out of the well?

Practice

Linear Programming

Graph each system of inequalities. Name the coordinates of the vertices of the feasible region. Find the maximum and minimum values of the given function for this region.

1. $2x - 4 \leq y$ vertices: (3, 2),
$-2x - 4 \leq y$ (−3, 2), (0, −4);
$2 \geq y$ max = 8,
$f(x, y) = -2x + y$ min = −4

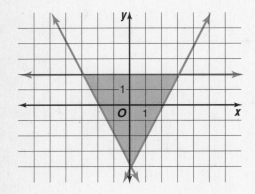

2. $3x - y \leq 7$ vertices: (4, 5),
$2x - y \geq 3$ (2, −1), (0, −3);
$y \geq x - 3$ max = 12,
$f(x, y) = x - 4y$ min = −16

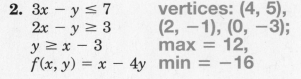
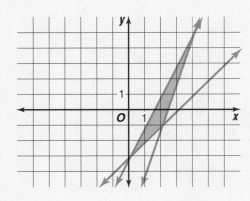

3. $x \geq 0$ vertices: (0, 0),
$y \geq 0$ (5, 0), (3, 6), (0, 6);
$3x + y \leq 15$ max = 15,
$y \leq 6$ min = 0
$f(x, y) = 3x + y$

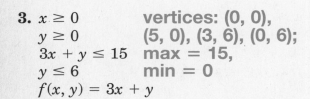
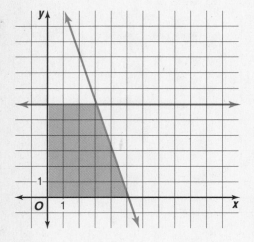

4. $x \leq 0$ vertices: (0, 0),
$y \leq 0$ (0, −7), $\left(-\frac{7}{4}, 0\right)$;
$4x + y \geq -7$
$f(x, y) = -x - 4y$ max = 28,
min = 0

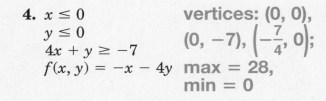
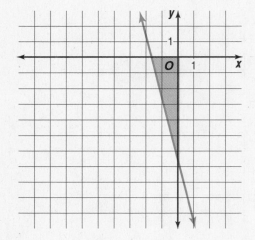

5. Solve a simpler problem.   A snail is at the bottom of a well that is 24 feet deep. The snail can climb 2 inches each hour, but then falls back 1 inch. How many hours will it take the snail to crawl out of the well? **287 hours**

NAME_____ DATE _____

Practice

Student Edition
Pages 160–164

Applications of Linear Programming

Solve.

1. The area of a parking lot is 600 square meters. A car requires 6 square meters. A bus requires 30 square meters. The attendant can handle only 60 vehicles. If a car is charged $2.50 and a bus $7.50, how many of each should be accepted to maximize income?

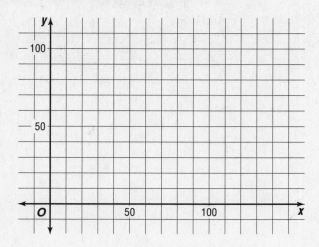

2. The cost to run Machine 1 for an hour is $2. During that hour, Machine 1 produces 240 bolts and 100 nuts. The cost to run Machine 2 for an hour is $2.40. During that hour, Machine 2 produces 160 bolts and 160 nuts. With a combined running time of no more than 30 hours, how long should each machine run to produce an order of at least 2080 bolts and 1520 nuts at the minimum operating cost?

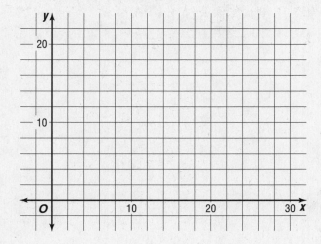

NAME_____ DATE _____

Practice

Applications of Linear Programming

Solve.

1. The area of a parking lot is 600 square meters. A car requires 6 square meters. A bus requires 30 square meters. The attendant can handle only 60 vehicles. If a car is charged $2.50 and a bus $7.50, how many of each should be accepted to maximize income?

50 cars, 10 buses

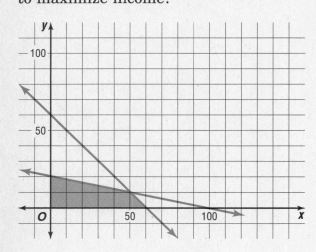

2. The cost to run Machine 1 for an hour is $2. During that hour, Machine 1 produces 240 bolts and 100 nuts. The cost to run Machine 2 for an hour is $2.40. During that hour, Machine 2 produces 160 bolts and 160 nuts. With a combined running time of no more than 30 hours, how long should each machine run to produce an order of at least 2080 bolts and 1520 nuts at the minimum operating cost?

Machine 1: 4 hours
Machine 2: 7 hours

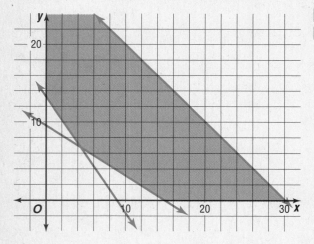

Practice

Solving Systems of Equations in Three Variables

Solve each system of equations.

1. $2x - y + 2z = 15$
$-x + y + z = 3$
$3x - y + 2z = 18$

2. $x - 4y + 3z = -27$
$2x + 2y - 3z = 22$
$4z = -16$

3. $a + b = 3$
$-b + c = 3$
$a + 2c = 10$

4. $3x - 2y + 4z = 15$
$x - y + z = 3$
$x + 4y - 5z = 0$

5. $2x + 3y + 4z = 2$
$5x - 2y + 3z = 0$
$x - 5y - 2z = -4$

6. $2x + y - z = -8$
$4x - y + 2z = -3$
$-3x + y + 2z = 5$

7. $2x - 5y + z = 5$
$3x + 2y - z = 17$
$4x - 3y + 2z = 17$

8. $p + 4r = -7$
$p - 3q = -8$
$q + r = 1$

9. The sum of three numbers is 6. The third number is the sum of the first and second number. The first number is one more than the third number. Find the numbers.

10. The sum of three numbers is -4. The second number decreased by the third is equal to the first. The sum of the first and second number is -5. Find the numbers.

Practice

Solving Systems of Equations in Three Variables

Solve each system of equations.

1. $2x - y + 2z = 15$
$-x + y + z = 3$
$3x - y + 2z = 18$ **(3, 1, 5)**

2. $x - 4y + 3z = -27$
$2x + 2y - 3z = 22$
$4z = -16$ **(1, 4, −4)**

3. $a + b = 3$
$-b + c = 3$
$a + 2c = 10$ **(2, 1, 4)**

4. $3x - 2y + 4z = 15$
$x - y + z = 3$
$x + 4y - 5z = 0$ **(3, 3, 3)**

5. $2x + 3y + 4z = 2$
$5x - 2y + 3z = 0$
$x - 5y - 2z = -4$ **(2, 2, −2)**

6. $2x + y - z = -8$
$4x - y + 2z = -3$
$-3x + y + 2z = 5$ **(−2, −3, 1)**

7. $2x - 5y + z = 5$
$3x + 2y - z = 17$
$4x - 3y + 2z = 17$ **(5, 1, 0)**

8. $p + 4r = -7$
$p - 3q = -8$
$q + r = 1$ **(1, 3, −2)**

9. The sum of three numbers is 6. The third number is the sum of the first and second number. The first number is one more than the third number. Find the numbers.
first = 4, second = −1, third = 3

10. The sum of three numbers is −4. The second number decreased by the third is equal to the first. The sum of the first and second number is −5. Find the numbers.
first = −3, second = −2, third = 1

NAME_____ DATE _____

Practice

An Introduction to Matrices

Perform the indicated operation.

1. $4\begin{bmatrix} 1 & 5 & 9 \\ 3 & 6 & 3 \\ 0 & 7 & 2 \end{bmatrix}$

2. $-1\begin{bmatrix} 6 & -4 \\ 3 & -2 \\ 5 & -5 \end{bmatrix}$

3. $\dfrac{1}{2}\begin{bmatrix} -8 & 0 \\ 2 & -12 \\ 6 & -14 \end{bmatrix}$

4. $-1.1\begin{bmatrix} 0.75 & 0.1 \\ 0.99 & 0.7 \end{bmatrix}$

Solve for the variables.

5. $\begin{bmatrix} 3x & 4y \\ -48 & 49 \end{bmatrix} = \begin{bmatrix} 27 & -16 \\ -3w & 7z \end{bmatrix}$

6. $\begin{bmatrix} 3x \\ y+4 \end{bmatrix} = \begin{bmatrix} y+8 \\ 17 \end{bmatrix}$

7. $x\begin{bmatrix} 2 & -5 \\ 7 & y \end{bmatrix} = \begin{bmatrix} 8 & -20 \\ z & 24 \end{bmatrix}$

8. $5\begin{bmatrix} x & y+2 \\ 6 & z \end{bmatrix} = \begin{bmatrix} 10 & 25 \\ 2z & 30x+5y \end{bmatrix}$

9. **Use Matrix Logic.** The Peterson children are 13, 14, and 15 years old. One collects stamps, one collects coins, and one collects shells. From the clues, find each child's age and what he or she collects.

   - The oldest collects stamps.
   - Bart collects coins.
   - Annette is older than Cassie.
   - The 14-year-old does not collect coins.

22

NAME _____ DATE _____

Practice

An Introduction to Matrices

Perform the indicated operation.

1. $4\begin{bmatrix} 1 & 5 & 9 \\ 3 & 6 & 3 \\ 0 & 7 & 2 \end{bmatrix}$ $\begin{bmatrix} 4 & 20 & 36 \\ 12 & 24 & 12 \\ 0 & 28 & 8 \end{bmatrix}$

2. $-1\begin{bmatrix} 6 & -4 \\ 3 & -2 \\ 5 & -5 \end{bmatrix}$ $\begin{bmatrix} -6 & 4 \\ -3 & 2 \\ -5 & 5 \end{bmatrix}$

3. $\frac{1}{2}\begin{bmatrix} -8 & 0 \\ 2 & -12 \\ 6 & -14 \end{bmatrix}$ $\begin{bmatrix} -4 & 0 \\ 1 & -6 \\ 3 & -7 \end{bmatrix}$

4. $-1.1\begin{bmatrix} 0.75 & 0.1 \\ 0.99 & 0.7 \end{bmatrix}$ $\begin{bmatrix} -0.825 & -0.11 \\ -1.089 & -0.77 \end{bmatrix}$

Solve for the variables.

5. $\begin{bmatrix} 3x & 4y \\ -48 & 49 \end{bmatrix} = \begin{bmatrix} 27 & -16 \\ -3w & 7z \end{bmatrix}$

   $x = 9, y = -4, w = 16, z = 7$

6. $\begin{bmatrix} 3x \\ y+4 \end{bmatrix} = \begin{bmatrix} y+8 \\ 17 \end{bmatrix}$

   $x = 7, y = 13$

7. $x\begin{bmatrix} 2 & -5 \\ 7 & y \end{bmatrix} = \begin{bmatrix} 8 & -20 \\ z & 24 \end{bmatrix}$

   $x = 4, y = 6, z = 28$

8. $5\begin{bmatrix} x & y+2 \\ 6 & z \end{bmatrix} = \begin{bmatrix} 10 & 25 \\ 2z & 30x+5y \end{bmatrix}$

   $x = 2, y = 3, z = 15$

9. Use Matrix Logic. The Peterson children are 13, 14, and
   15 years old. One collects stamps, one collects coins, and
   one collects shells. From the clues, find each child's age
   and what he or she collects.

   - The oldest collects stamps.
   - Bart collects coins.
   - Annette is older than Cassie.
   - The 14-year-old does not collect coins.

	13	14	15	stamps	coins	shells
Annette		✔	✔			
Bart	✔				✔	
Cassie		✔				✔

Algebra 2

NAME_____ DATE _____

Practice

Student Edition
Pages 194–198

Adding and Subtracting Matrices

Perform the indicated operations.

1. $3\begin{bmatrix} 1 & 5 \\ -1 & -5 \end{bmatrix} + 4\begin{bmatrix} -4 & -3 \\ -2 & -1 \end{bmatrix}$

2. $\begin{bmatrix} 2 & -1 \\ 3 & 7 \\ 14 & -9 \end{bmatrix} + \begin{bmatrix} -6 & 9 \\ 7 & -11 \\ -8 & 17 \end{bmatrix}$

3. $6\begin{bmatrix} 1 \\ -3 \\ 0 \end{bmatrix} + 5\begin{bmatrix} 2 \\ 7 \\ -8 \end{bmatrix} - 3\begin{bmatrix} -1 \\ 4 \\ 12 \end{bmatrix}$

4. $6\begin{bmatrix} 2 & 3 \\ -1 & 4 \\ 8 & -6 \end{bmatrix} + 5\begin{bmatrix} 7 & -4 \\ 3 & 2 \\ 0 & -1 \end{bmatrix}$

5. $7\begin{bmatrix} 2 & -1 & 8 \\ 4 & 7 & 9 \end{bmatrix} - 2\begin{bmatrix} -1 & 4 & -3 \\ 7 & 2 & -6 \end{bmatrix}$

6. $\dfrac{3}{4}\begin{bmatrix} 8 & 12 \\ -16 & 20 \end{bmatrix} + \dfrac{2}{3}\begin{bmatrix} 27 & -9 \\ 54 & -18 \end{bmatrix}$

7. $\dfrac{1}{2}\begin{bmatrix} 6 & 12 \\ 4 & 24 \end{bmatrix} - \dfrac{1}{4}\begin{bmatrix} 8 & 16 \\ 0 & 44 \end{bmatrix}$

8. $\dfrac{1}{2}\begin{bmatrix} -4 & -8 \\ 100 & 200 \\ 50 & 80 \end{bmatrix} + \begin{bmatrix} 5 & 10 \\ 20 & 30 \\ 40 & 60 \end{bmatrix}$

Solve for the variables.

9. $\begin{bmatrix} 2x \\ x \end{bmatrix} - \begin{bmatrix} 8y \\ y \end{bmatrix} = \begin{bmatrix} 12 \\ 1 \end{bmatrix}$

10. $\begin{bmatrix} y \\ y \end{bmatrix} + \begin{bmatrix} 8 \\ 4 \end{bmatrix} = \begin{bmatrix} 3x \\ 17 \end{bmatrix}$

NAME_____ DATE _____

Practice

Adding and Subtracting Matrices

Perform the indicated operations.

1. $3\begin{bmatrix} 1 & 5 \\ -1 & -5 \end{bmatrix} + 4\begin{bmatrix} -4 & -3 \\ -2 & -1 \end{bmatrix}$

$\begin{bmatrix} -13 & 3 \\ -11 & -19 \end{bmatrix}$

2. $\begin{bmatrix} 2 & -1 \\ 3 & 7 \\ 14 & -9 \end{bmatrix} + \begin{bmatrix} -6 & 9 \\ 7 & -11 \\ -8 & 17 \end{bmatrix}$

$\begin{bmatrix} -4 & 8 \\ 10 & -4 \\ 6 & 8 \end{bmatrix}$

3. $6\begin{bmatrix} 1 \\ -3 \\ 0 \end{bmatrix} + 5\begin{bmatrix} 2 \\ 7 \\ -8 \end{bmatrix} - 3\begin{bmatrix} -1 \\ 4 \\ 12 \end{bmatrix}$

$\begin{bmatrix} 19 \\ 5 \\ -76 \end{bmatrix}$

4. $6\begin{bmatrix} 2 & 3 \\ -1 & 4 \\ 8 & -6 \end{bmatrix} + 5\begin{bmatrix} 7 & -4 \\ 3 & 2 \\ 0 & -1 \end{bmatrix}$

$\begin{bmatrix} 47 & -2 \\ 9 & 34 \\ 48 & -41 \end{bmatrix}$

5. $7\begin{bmatrix} 2 & -1 & 8 \\ 4 & 7 & 9 \end{bmatrix} - 2\begin{bmatrix} -1 & 4 & -3 \\ 7 & 2 & -6 \end{bmatrix}$

$\begin{bmatrix} 16 & -15 & 62 \\ 14 & 45 & 75 \end{bmatrix}$

6. $\frac{3}{4}\begin{bmatrix} 8 & 12 \\ -16 & 20 \end{bmatrix} + \frac{2}{3}\begin{bmatrix} 27 & -9 \\ 54 & -18 \end{bmatrix}$

$\begin{bmatrix} 24 & 3 \\ 24 & 3 \end{bmatrix}$

7. $\frac{1}{2}\begin{bmatrix} 6 & 12 \\ 4 & 24 \end{bmatrix} - \frac{1}{4}\begin{bmatrix} 8 & 16 \\ 0 & 44 \end{bmatrix}$

$\begin{bmatrix} 1 & 2 \\ 2 & 1 \end{bmatrix}$

8. $\frac{1}{2}\begin{bmatrix} -4 & -8 \\ 100 & 200 \\ 50 & 80 \end{bmatrix} + \begin{bmatrix} 5 & 10 \\ 20 & 30 \\ 40 & 60 \end{bmatrix}$

$\begin{bmatrix} 3 & 6 \\ 70 & 130 \\ 65 & 100 \end{bmatrix}$

Solve for the variables.

9. $\begin{bmatrix} 2x \\ x \end{bmatrix} - \begin{bmatrix} 8y \\ y \end{bmatrix} = \begin{bmatrix} 12 \\ 1 \end{bmatrix}$ $x = -\frac{2}{3}; y = -\frac{5}{3}$

10. $\begin{bmatrix} y \\ y \end{bmatrix} + \begin{bmatrix} 8 \\ 4 \end{bmatrix} = \begin{bmatrix} 3x \\ 17 \end{bmatrix}$ $x = 7; y = 13$

Algebra 2

NAME_____ DATE _____

Practice

Multiplying Matrices

Find the dimensions of each matrix M.

1. $A_{7 \times 4} \cdot B_{4 \times 3} = M$

2. $A_{3 \times 5} \cdot M = B_{3 \times 8}$

3. $M \cdot A_{1 \times 6} = B_{2 \times 6}$

Perform the indicated operations, if possible.

4. $2\begin{bmatrix} 2 & 4 \\ 3 & -1 \end{bmatrix} + 3\begin{bmatrix} -3 & 0 \\ 2 & 5 \end{bmatrix}$

5. $\begin{bmatrix} 2 & 4 \\ 3 & -1 \end{bmatrix} \cdot \begin{bmatrix} 3 & -2 & 7 \\ 6 & 0 & -5 \end{bmatrix}$

6. $\begin{bmatrix} 2 & 4 \\ 3 & -1 \end{bmatrix} \cdot \begin{bmatrix} -3 & 0 \\ 2 & 5 \end{bmatrix} + 2\begin{bmatrix} -3 & 0 \\ 2 & 5 \end{bmatrix}$

7. $\begin{bmatrix} 3 & -2 & 7 \\ 6 & 0 & -5 \end{bmatrix} \cdot \begin{bmatrix} 3 & -2 & 7 \\ 6 & 0 & -5 \end{bmatrix}$

8. $\begin{bmatrix} 2 & 4 \\ 7 & -1 \end{bmatrix} \cdot \begin{bmatrix} -3 & 0 \\ 2 & 5 \end{bmatrix}$

9. $\begin{bmatrix} -3 & 0 \\ 2 & 5 \end{bmatrix} \cdot \begin{bmatrix} 2 & 4 \\ 7 & -1 \end{bmatrix}$

Find the new coordinates of the vertices of each polygon after the polygon is rotated 90° counterclockwise about the origin.

10. triangle ABC with vertices $A(2, 5)$, $B(5, 8)$, $C(3, 15)$

11. square $DEFG$ with vertices $D(-1, 2)$, $E(-1, -2)$, $F(3, -2)$, $G(3, 2)$

12. rectangle $HIJK$ with vertices $H(-1, 1)$, $I(1, -1)$, $J(7, 5)$, $K(5, 7)$

4-3

Practice

Multiplying Matrices

Find the dimensions of each matrix M.

1. $A_{7 \times 4} \cdot B_{4 \times 3} = M$

7×3

2. $A_{3 \times 5} \cdot M = B_{3 \times 8}$

5×8

3. $M \cdot A_{1 \times 6} = B_{2 \times 6}$

2×1

Perform the indicated operations, if possible.

4. $2\begin{bmatrix} 2 & 4 \\ 3 & -1 \end{bmatrix} + 3\begin{bmatrix} -3 & 0 \\ 2 & 5 \end{bmatrix}$

$\begin{bmatrix} -5 & 8 \\ 12 & 13 \end{bmatrix}$

5. $\begin{bmatrix} 2 & 4 \\ 3 & -1 \end{bmatrix} \cdot \begin{bmatrix} 3 & -2 & 7 \\ 6 & 0 & -5 \end{bmatrix}$

$\begin{bmatrix} 30 & -4 & -6 \\ 3 & -6 & 26 \end{bmatrix}$

6. $\begin{bmatrix} 2 & 4 \\ 3 & -1 \end{bmatrix} \cdot \begin{bmatrix} -3 & 0 \\ 2 & 5 \end{bmatrix} + 2\begin{bmatrix} -3 & 0 \\ 2 & 5 \end{bmatrix}$

$\begin{bmatrix} -4 & 20 \\ -7 & 5 \end{bmatrix}$

7. $\begin{bmatrix} 3 & -2 & 7 \\ 6 & 0 & -5 \end{bmatrix} \cdot \begin{bmatrix} 3 & -2 & 7 \\ 6 & 0 & -5 \end{bmatrix}$

not possible to evaluate

8. $\begin{bmatrix} 2 & 4 \\ 7 & -1 \end{bmatrix} \cdot \begin{bmatrix} -3 & 0 \\ 2 & 5 \end{bmatrix}$

$\begin{bmatrix} 2 & 20 \\ -23 & -5 \end{bmatrix}$

9. $\begin{bmatrix} -3 & 0 \\ 2 & 5 \end{bmatrix} \cdot \begin{bmatrix} 2 & 4 \\ 7 & -1 \end{bmatrix}$

$\begin{bmatrix} -6 & -12 \\ 39 & 3 \end{bmatrix}$

Find the new coordinates of the vertices of each polygon after the polygon is rotated 90° counterclockwise about the origin.

10. triangle ABC with vertices $A(2, 5)$, $B(5, 8)$, $C(3, 15)$

$(-5, 2)$, $(-8, 5)$, $(-15, 3)$

11. square $DEFG$ with vertices $D(-1, 2)$, $E(-1, -2)$, $F(3, -2)$, $G(3, 2)$

$(-2, -1)$, $(2, -1)$, $(2, 3)$, $(-2, 3)$

12. rectangle $HIJK$ with vertices $H(-1, 1)$, $I(1, -1)$, $J(7, 5)$, $K(5, 7)$

$(-1, -1)$, $(1, 1)$, $(-5, 7)$, $(-7, 5)$

4-4

Practice

Matrices and Determinants

Determine the value of the determinant of each matrix.

1. $\begin{bmatrix} -5 & 2 \\ -8 & -7 \end{bmatrix}$

2. $\begin{bmatrix} -2 & 3 & 1 \\ 0 & 4 & -3 \\ 2 & 5 & -1 \end{bmatrix}$

3. $\begin{bmatrix} 0 & -4 & 0 \\ 2 & -1 & 1 \\ 3 & -2 & 5 \end{bmatrix}$

4. $\begin{bmatrix} 2 & -4 & 1 \\ 3 & 0 & 9 \\ -1 & 5 & 7 \end{bmatrix}$

5. $\begin{bmatrix} 3 & -4 \\ 7 & 9 \end{bmatrix}$

6. $\begin{bmatrix} 2 & 7 & -6 \\ 8 & 4 & 0 \\ 1 & -1 & 3 \end{bmatrix}$

Solve for the variable.

7. $\begin{vmatrix} 3 & -4 \\ 2x & 5 \end{vmatrix} = 30$

8. $\begin{vmatrix} 2 & -1 \\ 3 & 4m \end{vmatrix} = -16$

9. $\begin{vmatrix} x & 3 & -1 \\ 2 & 1 & -2 \\ 4 & 1 & x \end{vmatrix} = 10$

10. $\begin{vmatrix} 2x & 0 & 3 \\ 7 & 5 & -1 \\ 4 & 2 & x \end{vmatrix} = 8x^2 - 3x + 12$

11. Find the area of a triangle whose vertices have coordinates $(3, 5)$, $(6, -5)$, and $(-4, 10)$.

12. Find the area of a triangle whose vertices have coordinates $(-8, 10)$, $(6, 17)$, and $(2, -4)$.

Practice

Matrices and Determinants

Determine the value of the determinant of each matrix.

1. $\begin{bmatrix} -5 & 2 \\ -8 & -7 \end{bmatrix}$ **51**

2. $\begin{bmatrix} -2 & 3 & 1 \\ 0 & 4 & -3 \\ 2 & 5 & -1 \end{bmatrix}$ **−48**

3. $\begin{bmatrix} 0 & -4 & 0 \\ 2 & -1 & 1 \\ 3 & -2 & 5 \end{bmatrix}$ **28**

4. $\begin{bmatrix} 2 & -4 & 1 \\ 3 & 0 & 9 \\ -1 & 5 & 7 \end{bmatrix}$ **45**

5. $\begin{bmatrix} 3 & -4 \\ 7 & 9 \end{bmatrix}$ **55**

6. $\begin{bmatrix} 2 & 7 & -6 \\ 8 & 4 & 0 \\ 1 & -1 & 3 \end{bmatrix}$ **−72**

Solve for the variable.

7. $\begin{vmatrix} 3 & -4 \\ 2x & 5 \end{vmatrix} = 30$ $x = \dfrac{15}{8}$

8. $\begin{vmatrix} 2 & -1 \\ 3 & 4m \end{vmatrix} = -16$ $m = -\dfrac{19}{8}$

9. $\begin{vmatrix} x & 3 & -1 \\ 2 & 1 & -2 \\ 4 & 1 & x \end{vmatrix} = 10$ $x = 8$ or $x = -4$

10. $\begin{vmatrix} 2x & 0 & 3 \\ 7 & 5 & -1 \\ 4 & 2 & x \end{vmatrix} = 8x^2 - 3x + 12$

$x = \dfrac{5}{2}$ or $x = -6$

11. Find the area of a triangle whose vertices have coordinates (3, 5), (6, −5), and (−4, 10).
    27.5 units²

12. Find the area of a triangle whose vertices have coordinates (−8, 10), (6, 17), and (2, −4).
    133 units²

Practice

Student Edition
Pages 212–218

Identity and Inverse Matrices

Find the inverse of each matrix, if it exists.

1. $\begin{bmatrix} 3 & 1 \\ -4 & 2 \end{bmatrix}$

2. $\begin{bmatrix} 4 & 5 \\ -4 & -3 \end{bmatrix}$

3. $\begin{bmatrix} 4 & 6 \\ 6 & 9 \end{bmatrix}$

4. $\begin{bmatrix} 2 & 5 \\ -1 & 3 \end{bmatrix}$

5. $\begin{bmatrix} -4 & 7 \\ 8 & 1 \end{bmatrix}$

6. $\begin{bmatrix} 2 & 0 \\ 3 & 5 \end{bmatrix}$

7. $\begin{bmatrix} 2 & -5 \\ 3 & 1 \end{bmatrix}$

8. $\begin{bmatrix} -1 & 3 \\ 4 & -7 \end{bmatrix}$

NAME _____ DATE _____

Practice

Student Edition
Pages 212–218

Identity and Inverse Matrices

Find the inverse of each matrix, if it exists.

1. $\begin{bmatrix} 3 & 1 \\ -4 & 2 \end{bmatrix}$

$\begin{bmatrix} \dfrac{1}{5} & -\dfrac{1}{10} \\ \dfrac{2}{5} & \dfrac{3}{10} \end{bmatrix}$

2. $\begin{bmatrix} 4 & 5 \\ -4 & -3 \end{bmatrix}$

$\begin{bmatrix} -\dfrac{3}{8} & -\dfrac{5}{8} \\ \dfrac{1}{2} & \dfrac{1}{2} \end{bmatrix}$

3. $\begin{bmatrix} 4 & 6 \\ 6 & 9 \end{bmatrix}$

does not exist

4. $\begin{bmatrix} 2 & 5 \\ -1 & 3 \end{bmatrix}$

$\begin{bmatrix} \dfrac{3}{11} & -\dfrac{5}{11} \\ \dfrac{1}{11} & \dfrac{2}{11} \end{bmatrix}$

5. $\begin{bmatrix} -4 & 7 \\ 8 & 1 \end{bmatrix}$

$\begin{bmatrix} -\dfrac{1}{60} & \dfrac{7}{60} \\ \dfrac{2}{15} & \dfrac{1}{15} \end{bmatrix}$

6. $\begin{bmatrix} 2 & 0 \\ 3 & 5 \end{bmatrix}$

$\begin{bmatrix} \dfrac{1}{2} & 0 \\ -\dfrac{3}{10} & \dfrac{1}{5} \end{bmatrix}$

7. $\begin{bmatrix} 2 & -5 \\ 3 & 1 \end{bmatrix}$

$\begin{bmatrix} \dfrac{1}{17} & \dfrac{5}{17} \\ -\dfrac{3}{17} & \dfrac{2}{17} \end{bmatrix}$

8. $\begin{bmatrix} -1 & 3 \\ 4 & -7 \end{bmatrix}$

$\begin{bmatrix} \dfrac{7}{5} & \dfrac{3}{5} \\ \dfrac{4}{5} & \dfrac{1}{5} \end{bmatrix}$

Practice

Using Matrices to Solve Systems of Equations

Write the system of linear equations represented by each matrix equation.

1. $\begin{bmatrix} 3 & -2 & 5 \\ 1 & 1 & -4 \\ -2 & 2 & 7 \end{bmatrix} \cdot \begin{bmatrix} x \\ y \\ z \end{bmatrix} = \begin{bmatrix} 3 \\ 2 \\ -5 \end{bmatrix}$

2. $\begin{bmatrix} 2 & 1 & -3 \\ 5 & 2 & -2 \\ 3 & -3 & 5 \end{bmatrix} \cdot \begin{bmatrix} x \\ y \\ z \end{bmatrix} = \begin{bmatrix} -5 \\ 8 \\ 17 \end{bmatrix}$

Write a matrix equation for each system.

3. $-3x + 2y = 9$
   $5x - 3y = -13$

4. $6x - 2y = -2$
   $3x + 3y = 10$

Solve each matrix equation by using inverse matrices.

5. $\begin{bmatrix} 2 & 1 \\ 3 & 2 \end{bmatrix} \cdot \begin{bmatrix} x \\ y \end{bmatrix} = \begin{bmatrix} 0 \\ -2 \end{bmatrix}$

6. $\begin{bmatrix} 1 & 5 \\ 2 & -3 \end{bmatrix} \cdot \begin{bmatrix} x \\ y \end{bmatrix} = \begin{bmatrix} 10 \\ 7 \end{bmatrix}$

7. $\begin{bmatrix} 1 & 3 & 2 \\ -1 & 2 & 1 \\ 4 & 1 & -2 \end{bmatrix} \cdot \begin{bmatrix} x \\ y \\ z \end{bmatrix} = \begin{bmatrix} 2 \\ -1 \\ -1 \end{bmatrix}$

8. $\begin{bmatrix} 2 & 3 & -1 \\ 4 & 1 & 5 \\ 1 & 2 & -1 \end{bmatrix} \cdot \begin{bmatrix} x \\ y \\ z \end{bmatrix} = \begin{bmatrix} 17 \\ -9 \\ 12 \end{bmatrix}$

Practice

Using Matrices to Solve Systems of Equations

Write the system of linear equations represented by each matrix equation.

1. $\begin{bmatrix} 3 & -2 & 5 \\ 1 & 1 & -4 \\ -2 & 2 & 7 \end{bmatrix} \cdot \begin{bmatrix} x \\ y \\ z \end{bmatrix} = \begin{bmatrix} 3 \\ 2 \\ -5 \end{bmatrix}$

   $3x - 2y + 5z = 3$
   $x + y - 4z = 2$
   $-2x + 2y + 7z = -5$

2. $\begin{bmatrix} 2 & 1 & -3 \\ 5 & 2 & -2 \\ 3 & -3 & 5 \end{bmatrix} \cdot \begin{bmatrix} x \\ y \\ z \end{bmatrix} = \begin{bmatrix} -5 \\ 8 \\ 17 \end{bmatrix}$

   $2x + y - 3z = -5$
   $5x + 2y - 2z = 8$
   $3x - 3y + 5z = 17$

Write a matrix equation for each system.

3. $-3x + 2y = 9$
   $5x - 3y = -13$

$\begin{bmatrix} -3 & 2 \\ 5 & -3 \end{bmatrix} \cdot \begin{bmatrix} x \\ y \end{bmatrix} = \begin{bmatrix} 9 \\ -13 \end{bmatrix}$

4. $6x - 2y = -2$
   $3x + 3y = 10$

$\begin{bmatrix} 6 & -2 \\ 3 & 3 \end{bmatrix} \cdot \begin{bmatrix} x \\ y \end{bmatrix} = \begin{bmatrix} -2 \\ 10 \end{bmatrix}$

Solve each matrix equation by using inverse matrices.

5. $\begin{bmatrix} 2 & 1 \\ 3 & 2 \end{bmatrix} \cdot \begin{bmatrix} x \\ y \end{bmatrix} = \begin{bmatrix} 0 \\ -2 \end{bmatrix}$ $M^{-1} = \begin{bmatrix} 2 & -1 \\ -3 & 2 \end{bmatrix}$; $(2, -4)$

6. $\begin{bmatrix} 1 & 5 \\ 2 & -3 \end{bmatrix} \cdot \begin{bmatrix} x \\ y \end{bmatrix} = \begin{bmatrix} 10 \\ 7 \end{bmatrix}$ $M^{-1} = -\frac{1}{13}\begin{bmatrix} -3 & -5 \\ -2 & 1 \end{bmatrix}$; $(5, 1)$

7. $\begin{bmatrix} 1 & 3 & 2 \\ -1 & 2 & 1 \\ 4 & 1 & -2 \end{bmatrix} \cdot \begin{bmatrix} x \\ y \\ z \end{bmatrix} = \begin{bmatrix} 2 \\ -1 \\ -1 \end{bmatrix}$ $M^{-1} = -\frac{1}{17}\begin{bmatrix} -5 & 8 & -1 \\ 2 & -10 & -3 \\ -9 & 11 & 5 \end{bmatrix}$; $(1, -1, 2)$

8. $\begin{bmatrix} 2 & 3 & -1 \\ 4 & 1 & 5 \\ 1 & 2 & -1 \end{bmatrix} \cdot \begin{bmatrix} x \\ y \\ z \end{bmatrix} = \begin{bmatrix} 17 \\ -9 \\ 12 \end{bmatrix}$ $M^{-1} = \frac{1}{2}\begin{bmatrix} 11 & -1 & -16 \\ -9 & 1 & 14 \\ -7 & 1 & 10 \end{bmatrix}$ $(2, 3, -4)$

Practice

Using Augmented Matrices

Solve each system of equations by using augmented matrices.

1. $5x + 9y = 19$
$2x - y = -20$

2. $2x + y - 3z = -3$
$3x + 2y + 4z = 5$
$-4x - y + 2z = 4$

3. $4x - 3y - z = -3$
$5x + 2y + 2z = 7$
$3x + 3y + z = 10$

4. $x + 2z = 11$
$2x + y = 4$
$x + 3y + z = 1$

5. $2x + y + z = 2$
$-x - y + 2z = 7$
$-3x + 2y + 3z = 7$

6. $3x - 2y + 5z = -14$
$x + 5y - 3z = 18$
$-2x - 3y + 8z = -8$

7. $2x - y + z = 4$
$x + y - z = 11$
$4x - 2y + 2z = 5$

8. $3x - 2y + 4z = 8$
$x + y - 3z = 1$
$6x - 4y + 8z = 16$

Using Augmented Matrices

Solve each system of equations by using augmented matrices.

1. $5x + 9y = 19$
$2x - y = -20$
$(-7, 6)$

2. $2x + y - 3z = -3$
$3x + 2y + 4z = 5$
$-4x - y + 2z = 4$
$(-1, 2, 1)$

3. $4x - 3y - z = -3$
$5x + 2y + 2z = 7$
$3x + 3y + z = 10$
$(1, 3, -2)$

4. $x + 2z = 11$
$2x + y = 4$
$x + 3y + z = 1$
$(3, -2, 4)$

5. $2x + y + z = 2$
$-x - y + 2z = 7$
$-3x + 2y + 3z = 7$
$(0, -1, 3)$

6. $3x - 2y + 5z = -14$
$x + 5y - 3z = 18$
$-2x - 3y + 8z = -8$
$(-2, 4, 0)$

7. $2x - y + z = 4$
$x + y - z = 11$
$4x - 2y + 2z = 5$
$\emptyset$

8. $3x - 2y + 4z = 8$
$x + y - 3z = 1$
$6x - 4y + 8z = 16$
$\left(\frac{2}{5}z + 2, \frac{13}{5}z - 1, z\right)$

NAME_____ DATE _____

Practice

Integration: Statistics
Box-and-Whisker Plots

Find the range, quartiles, interquartile range, and outliers for each set of data.

1. {4, 7, 9, 2, 8, 16, 21, 10, 5, 11}

2. {25, 46, 39, 27, 50, 56, 92, 48, 56, 10}

3. {43, 26, 92, 11, 8, 49, 52, 126, 86, 42, 63, 78, 91, 79, 86}

4. {1.6, 9.8, 4.5, 6.2, 8.7, 5.6, 3.9, 6.8, 9.7, 1.1, 4.7, 3.8, 7.5, 2.8, 0.1}

5. {146, 289, 121, 146, 212, 98, 86, 153, 128, 136, 181, 142}

The following chart gives the number of motorcycle fatalities in the United States by state and federal district in a recent year.

AL	39	FL	235	LA	45	NE	31	OK	46	VT	12
AK	1	GA	63	ME	21	NV	22	OR	70	VA	56
AZ	91	HI	13	MD	65	NH	24	PA	150	WA	90
AR	50	ID	27	MA	62	NJ	49	RI	18	WV	27
CA	767	IL	174	MI	105	NM	37	SC	56	WI	88
CO	62	IN	131	MN	54	NY	181	SD	14	WY	5
CT	65	IA	57	MS	30	NC	91	TN	83		
DE	14	KS	42	MO	60	ND	7	TX	297		
DC	4	KY	40	MT	26	OH	199	UT	30		

1. Make a box-and-whisker plot of the data.

2. Identify any outliers.

Algebra 2

Integration: Statistics
Box-and-Whisker Plots

Find the range, quartiles, interquartile range, and outliers for each set of data.

1. {4, 7, 9, 2, 8, 16, 21, 10, 5, 11}
   19; 5, 8.5, 11; 6; 21

2. {25, 46, 39, 27, 50, 56, 92, 48, 56, 10}
   82; 27, 47, 56; 29; none

3. {43, 26, 92, 11, 8, 49, 52, 126, 86, 42, 63, 78, 91, 79, 86}
   118; 42, 63, 86; 44; none

4. {1.6, 9.8, 4.5, 6.2, 8.7, 5.6, 3.9, 6.8, 9.7, 1.1, 4.7, 3.8, 7.5, 2.8, 0.1}
   9.7; 2.8, 4.7, 7.5; 4.7; none

5. {146, 289, 121, 146, 212, 98, 86, 153, 128, 136, 181, 142}
   203; 124.5, 144, 167; 42.5; 289

The following chart gives the number of motorcycle fatalities in the United States by state and federal district in a recent year.

AL	39	FL	235	LA	45	NE	31	OK	46	VT	12
AK	1	GA	63	ME	21	NV	22	OR	70	VA	56
AZ	91	HI	13	MD	65	NH	24	PA	150	WA	90
AR	50	ID	27	MA	62	NJ	49	RI	18	WV	27
CA	767	IL	174	MI	105	NM	37	SC	56	WI	88
CO	62	IN	131	MN	54	NY	181	SD	14	WY	5
CT	65	IA	57	MS	30	NC	91	TN	83		
DE	14	KS	42	MO	60	ND	7	TX	297		
DC	4	KY	40	MT	26	OH	199	UT	30		

1. Make a box-and-whisker plot of the data. **LV: 1, LQ: 26, M: 50, UQ: 88, GV: 181**

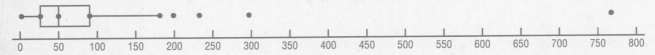

2. Identify any outliers. **199, 235, 297, 767**

Practice

Monomials

Simplify. Assume that no variable equals 0.

1. $3n^2v^3 - n^2v^3 + 8v^3n^2$

2. $4r^6w^2 + 9r^2w^6 - r^6w^2$

3. $y^7 \cdot y^3 \cdot y^2$

4. $(n^6)^3$

5. $(2n)^4 + 2n^4$

6. $\dfrac{12m^8y^6}{-9my^4}$

7. $(4a^3c^2)^3(-3ac^4)^2$

8. $\left(\dfrac{3}{2}e^2f^4\right)^4\left(-\dfrac{4}{3}e^5f\right)^3\left(-\dfrac{1}{6}ef^5\right)$

9. $-5v^2(2r^3v^2)(rv^3) - (-r^2)(16r^2v^7)$

10. $(-n)^4(2xy^2n)^3 + (4xy^3n^2)^2(-3xn^3)$

11. $\dfrac{(3x^{-2}y^3)(5xy^{-8})}{(x^{-3})^4y^{-2}}$

12. $(m^4n^6)^4(m^3n^2p^5)^6$

13. $(3x^2y)(2xy^4) + (4xy^2)(3x^2y^3)$

14. $t^{-5}(t^2 - t^4 + 5t)$

15. $\dfrac{-20(m^2v)(-v)^3}{5(-v)^2(-m^4)}$

16. $\dfrac{x^{7y+1}}{x^{7y-5}}$

Evaluate. Express each answer in both scientific and decimal notation.

17. $(4.8 \times 10^2)(6.9 \times 10^4)$

18. $(3.7 \times 10^9)(8.7 \times 10^2)$

19. $\dfrac{4 \times 10^8}{1.6 \times 10^4}$

20. $\dfrac{2.7 \times 10^6}{9 \times 10^{10}}$

Monomials

Simplify. Assume that no variable equals 0.

1. $3n^2v^3 - n^2v^3 + 8v^3n^2$ $\quad \mathbf{10n^2v^3}$

2. $4r^6w^2 + 9r^2w^6 - r^6w^2$ $\quad \mathbf{3r^6w^2 + 9r^2w^6}$

3. $y^7 \cdot y^3 \cdot y^2$ $\quad \mathbf{y^{12}}$

4. $(n^6)^3$ $\quad \mathbf{n^{18}}$

5. $(2n)^4 + 2n^4$ $\quad \mathbf{18n^4}$

6. $\dfrac{12m^8y^6}{-9my^4}$ $\quad \mathbf{\dfrac{4m^7y^2}{-3}}$

7. $(4a^3c^2)^3(-3ac^4)^2$ $\quad \mathbf{576a^{11}c^{14}}$

8. $\left(\dfrac{3}{2}e^2f^4\right)^4\left(-\dfrac{4}{3}e^5f\right)^3\left(-\dfrac{1}{6}ef^5\right)$ $\quad \mathbf{2e^{24}f^{24}}$

9. $-5v^2(2r^3v^2)(rv^3) - (-r^2)(16r^2v^7)$
$\quad \mathbf{6r^4v^7}$

10. $(-n)^4(2xy^2n)^3 + (4xy^3n^2)^2(-3xn^3)$
$\quad \mathbf{-40x^3y^6n^7}$

11. $\dfrac{(3x^{-2}y^3)(5xy^{-8})}{(x^{-3})^4y^{-2}}$ $\quad \mathbf{\dfrac{15x^{11}}{y^3}}$

12. $(m^4n^6)^4(m^3n^2p^5)^6$ $\quad \mathbf{m^{34}n^{36}p^{30}}$

13. $(3x^2y)(2xy^4) + (4xy^2)(3x^2y^3)$
$\quad \mathbf{18x^3y^5}$

14. $t^{-5}(t^2 - t^4 + 5t)$ $\quad \mathbf{\dfrac{1}{t^3} - \dfrac{1}{t} + \dfrac{5}{t^4}}$

15. $\dfrac{-20(m^2v)(-v)^3}{5(-v)^2(-m^4)}$ $\quad \mathbf{-\dfrac{4v^2}{m^2}}$

16. $\dfrac{x^{7y+1}}{x^{7y-5}}$ $\quad \mathbf{x^6}$

Evaluate. Express each answer in both scientific and decimal notation.

17. $(4.8 \times 10^2)(6.9 \times 10^4)$
$\quad \mathbf{3.312 \times 10^7;\ 33{,}120{,}000}$

18. $(3.7 \times 10^9)(8.7 \times 10^2)$
$\quad \mathbf{3.219 \times 10^{12};\ 3{,}219{,}000{,}000{,}000}$

19. $\dfrac{4 \times 10^8}{1.6 \times 10^4}$
$\quad \mathbf{2.5 \times 10^4;\ 25{,}000}$

20. $\dfrac{2.7 \times 10^6}{9 \times 10^{10}}$
$\quad \mathbf{3 \times 10^{-5};\ 0.00003}$

Practice

Polynomials

Simplify.

1. $(-6n - 13n^2) + (-3n + 9n^2)$

2. $(8x^2 - 3x) - (4x^2 + 5x - 3)$

3. $(5m^2 - 2mp - 6p^2) - (-3m^2 + 5mp + p^2)$

4. $-9(y - 7w) + 4(2y + w)$

5. $-6a^2w(a^3w - aw^4)$

6. $-9r^4y^2(-3ry^7 + 2r^3y^4 - 8r^{10})$

7. $5a^2w^3(a^2w^6 - 3a^4w^2 + 9aw^6)$

8. $2x^2(x - 1) + (x + 1)^2$

9. $(v^2 - 6)(v^2 + 4)$

10. $(7a + 9y)(2a - y)$

11. $(y - 8)^2$

12. $(x^2 + 5y)^2$

13. $(5x + 4w)(5x - 4w)$

14. $(2n^4 - 3)(2n^4 + 3)$

15. $(x + y)(x^2 - 3xy + 2y^2)$

16. $u(u - 6)(u - 3)$

17. $(n - 3)(n + 4)(n - 1)$

18. $(a - r)^2(2a - 3r)$

19. $(2x + 3y)(4x - 6y + 7z)$

20. $(3a + 4b)^2$

NAME _____ DATE _____

Practice

Polynomials

Simplify.

1. $(-6n - 13n^2) + (-3n + 9n^2)$
   $-9n - 4n^2$

2. $(8x^2 - 3x) - (4x^2 + 5x - 3)$
   $4x^2 - 8x + 3$

3. $(5m^2 - 2mp - 6p^2) - (-3m^2 + 5mp + p^2)$
   $8m^2 - 7mp - 7p^2$

4. $-9(y - 7w) + 4(2y + w)$
   $-y + 67w$

5. $-6a^2w(a^3w - aw^4)$
   $-6a^5w^2 + 6a^3w^5$

6. $-9r^4y^2(-3ry^7 + 2r^3y^4 - 8r^{10})$
   $27r^5y^9 - 18r^7y^6 + 72r^{14}y^2$

7. $5a^2w^3(a^2w^6 - 3a^4w^2 + 9aw^6)$
   $5a^4w^9 - 15a^6w^5 + 45a^3w^9$

8. $2x^2(x - 1) + (x + 1)^2$
   $2x^3 - x^2 + 2x + 1$

9. $(v^2 - 6)(v^2 + 4)$
   $v^4 - 2v^2 - 24$

10. $(7a + 9y)(2a - y)$
    $14a^2 + 11ay - 9y^2$

11. $(y - 8)^2$
    $y^2 - 16y + 64$

12. $(x^2 + 5y)^2$
    $x^4 + 10x^2y + 25y^2$

13. $(5x + 4w)(5x - 4w)$
    $25x^2 - 16w^2$

14. $(2n^4 - 3)(2n^4 + 3)$
    $4n^8 - 9$

15. $(x + y)(x^2 - 3xy + 2y^2)$
    $x^3 - 2x^2y - xy^2 + 2y^3$

16. $u(u - 6)(u - 3)$
    $u^3 - 9u^2 + 18u$

17. $(n - 3)(n + 4)(n - 1)$
    $n^3 - 13n + 12$

18. $(a - r)^2(2a - 3r)$
    $2a^3 - 7a^2r + 8ar^2 - 3r^3$

19. $(2x + 3y)(4x - 6y + 7z)$
    $8x^2 + 14xz - 18y^2 + 21yz$

20. $(3a + 4b)^2$
    $9a^2 + 24ab + 16b^2$

NAME_____ DATE _____

Practice

Dividing Polynomials

Simplify.

1. $(-30x^3y + 12x^2y^2 - 18x^2y) \div (-6x^2y)$

2. $(2x^2 + 3x - 4) \div (x - 2)$

3. $(4x^2 - 2x + 6)(2x - 3)^{-1}$

4. $(x^4 - 3x^3 + 5x - 6) \div (x + 2)$

5. $(6x^2 - x - 7) \div (3x + 1)$

6. $(2x^3 + 4x - 6) \div (x + 3)$

Use synthetic division to find each quotient.

7. $(2r^3 + 5r^2 - 2r - 15) \div (2r - 3)$

8. $(x^4 - 20) \div (x + 2)$

Algebra 2

Practice

Dividing Polynomials

Simplify.

1. $(-30x^3y + 12x^2y^2 - 18x^2y) \div (-6x^2y)$
$5x - 2y + 3$

2. $(2x^2 + 3x - 4) \div (x - 2)$
$2x + 7 + \dfrac{10}{x - 2}$

3. $(4x^2 - 2x + 6)(2x - 3)^{-1}$
$2x + 2 + \dfrac{12}{2x - 3}$

4. $(x^4 - 3x^3 + 5x - 6) \div (x + 2)$
$x^3 - 5x^2 + 10x - 15 + \dfrac{24}{x + 2}$

5. $(6x^2 - x - 7) \div (3x + 1)$
$2x - 1 - \dfrac{6}{3x + 1}$

6. $(2x^3 + 4x - 6) \div (x + 3)$
$2x^2 - 6x + 22 - \dfrac{72}{x + 3}$

Use synthetic division to find each quotient.

7. $(2r^3 + 5r^2 - 2r - 15) \div (2r - 3)$
$r^2 + 4r + 5$

8. $(x^4 - 20) \div (x + 2)$
$x^3 - 2x^2 + 4x - 8 - \dfrac{4}{x + 2}$

Practice

Factoring

Factor completely.

1. $15a^2b - 10ab^2$

2. $2x^3y - x^2y + 5xy^2 + xy^3$

3. $16r^2 - 169$

4. $c^2 - 49$

5. $2y^2 - 242$

6. $x^3 + 8$

7. $8m^3 - 1$

8. $b^4 - 81$

9. $x^2 - 3x - 10$

10. $r^3 + 3r^2 - 54r$

11. $4a^2 + a - 3$

12. $2t^3 + 32t^2 + 128t$

13. $y^2 + 20y + 96$

14. $6n^2 - 11n - 2$

15. $x^2 - 8x + 16$

16. $21 - 7t + 3r - rt$

17. $x^2 + 2x - xy - 2y$

18. $x^2 + 2xy + 2x + y^2 + 2y - 8$

19. $4x^6 - 4x^2$

20. $k^3 - 2k^2r - 3kr^2$

21. $45x^2 - 80y^2$

22. $36a^3b^2 + 66a^2b^3 - 210ab^4$

23. $4a^2 + 12ab + 9b^2 - 25c^2$

24. $81x^4 - 16$

25. $5y^5 + 135y^2$

26. $18p^3 - 51p^2 - 135p$

Factoring

Factor completely.

1. $15a^2b - 10ab^2$
$5ab(3a - 2b)$

2. $2x^3y - x^2y + 5xy^2 + xy^3$
$xy(2x^2 - x + 5y + y^2)$

3. $16r^2 - 169$
$(4r + 13)(4r - 13)$

4. $c^2 - 49$
$(c + 7)(c - 7)$

5. $2y^2 - 242$
$2(y + 11)(y - 11)$

6. $x^3 + 8$
$(x + 2)(x^2 - 2x + 4)$

7. $8m^3 - 1$
$(2m - 1)(4m^2 + 2m + 1)$

8. $b^4 - 81$
$(b^2 + 9)(b + 3)(b - 3)$

9. $x^2 - 3x - 10$
$(x - 5)(x + 2)$

10. $r^3 + 3r^2 - 54r$
$r(r + 9)(r - 6)$

11. $4a^2 + a - 3$
$(4a - 3)(a + 1)$

12. $2t^3 + 32t^2 + 128t$
$2t(t + 8)^2$

13. $y^2 + 20y + 96$
$(y + 8)(y + 12)$

14. $6n^2 - 11n - 2$
$(6n + 1)(n - 2)$

15. $x^2 - 8x + 16$
$(x - 4)^2$

16. $21 - 7t + 3r - rt$
$(r + 7)(3 - t)$

17. $x^2 + 2x - xy - 2y$
$(x + 2)(x - y)$

18. $x^2 + 2xy + 2x + y^2 + 2y - 8$
$(x + y + 4)(x + y - 2)$

19. $4x^6 - 4x^2$
$4x^2(x^2 + 1)(x + 1)(x - 1)$

20. $k^3 - 2k^2r - 3kr^2$
$k(k - 3r)(k + r)$

21. $45x^2 - 80y^2$
$5(3x + 4y)(3x - 4y)$

22. $36a^3b^2 + 66a^2b^3 - 210ab^4$
$6ab^2(3a - 5b)(2a + 7b)$

23. $4a^2 + 12ab + 9b^2 - 25c^2$
$(2a + 3b + 5c)(2a + 3b - 5c)$

24. $81x^4 - 16$
$(9x^2 + 4)(3x + 2)(3x - 2)$

25. $5y^5 + 135y^2$
$5y^2(y + 3)(y^2 - 3y + 9)$

26. $18p^3 - 51p^2 - 135p$
$3p(2p - 9)(3p + 5)$

Practice

Roots of Real Numbers

Simplify.

1. $\sqrt[5]{32}$

2. $-\sqrt[4]{256}$

3. $\sqrt{x^2 + 10x + 25}$

4. $\sqrt[6]{(m + 4)^6}$

5. $\sqrt[3]{-64r^6w^{15}}$

6. $\sqrt{49m^2t^8}$

7. $\sqrt[4]{81}$

8. $\sqrt[3]{-64}$

9. $\sqrt{(2x)^8}$

10. $-\sqrt[4]{625}$

11. $\sqrt[3]{216}$

12. $\sqrt{676x^4y^6}$

13. $\sqrt[3]{(2x + 1)^3}$

14. $\sqrt[5]{-32x^5y^{10}}$

15. $-\sqrt{144m^8n^6}$

16. $\sqrt[3]{-27x^9y^{12}}$

17. $\sqrt[5]{243x^{10}}$

18. $-\sqrt{49a^{10}b^{16}}$

19. $\sqrt[4]{(x - 5)^8}$

20. $\sqrt[3]{343d^6}$

21. $\sqrt{0.81}$

22. $-\sqrt{0.0016}$

23. $\sqrt[3]{0.512}$

24. $-\sqrt[4]{0.6561}$

Use a calculator to approximate each value to three decimal places.

25. $\sqrt{7.8}$

26. $-\sqrt{89}$

27. $\sqrt[3]{25}$

28. $\sqrt[3]{-4}$

Practice

Roots of Real Numbers

Simplify.

1. $\sqrt[5]{32}$ **2**

2. $-\sqrt[4]{256}$ **− 4**

3. $\sqrt{x^2 + 10x + 25}$ **|x + 5|**

4. $\sqrt[6]{(m + 4)^6}$ **|m + 4|**

5. $\sqrt[3]{-64r^6w^{15}}$ **−4r²w⁵**

6. $\sqrt{49m^2t^8}$ **7|m|t⁴**

7. $\sqrt[4]{81}$ **3**

8. $\sqrt[3]{-64}$ **−4**

9. $\sqrt{(2x)^8}$ **16x⁴**

10. $-\sqrt[4]{625}$ **−5**

11. $\sqrt[3]{216}$ **6**

12. $\sqrt{676x^4y^6}$ **26x²|y³|**

13. $\sqrt[3]{(2x + 1)^3}$ **2x + 1**

14. $\sqrt[5]{-32x^5y^{10}}$ **−2xy²**

15. $-\sqrt{144m^8n^6}$ **−12m⁴|n³|**

16. $\sqrt[3]{-27x^9y^{12}}$ **−3x³y⁴**

17. $\sqrt[5]{243x^{10}}$ **3x²**

18. $-\sqrt{49a^{10}b^{16}}$ **−7|a⁵|b⁸**

19. $\sqrt[4]{(x - 5)^8}$ **(x − 5)²**

20. $\sqrt[3]{343d^6}$ **7d²**

21. $\sqrt{0.81}$ **0.9**

22. $-\sqrt{0.0016}$ **−0.04**

23. $\sqrt[3]{0.512}$ **0.8**

24. $-\sqrt[4]{0.6561}$ **−0.9**

Use a calculator to approximate each value to three decimal places.

25. $\sqrt{7.8}$ **2.793**

26. $-\sqrt{89}$ **−9.434**

27. $\sqrt[3]{25}$ **2.924**

28. $\sqrt[3]{-4}$ **−1.587**

Practice

Radical Expressions

Simplify.

1. $\sqrt[3]{-432}$

2. $\sqrt{540}$

3. $\sqrt{5}(\sqrt{10} - \sqrt{45})$

4. $\sqrt[3]{6}(4\sqrt[3]{12} + 5\sqrt[3]{9})$

5. $(2\sqrt[3]{24})(7\sqrt[3]{18})$

6. $\sqrt[4]{\dfrac{8}{9a^3}}$

7. $\sqrt{\dfrac{11}{9}}$

8. $\sqrt[3]{-6750}$

9. $\sqrt{3x^2y^3} \cdot \sqrt{75xy^5}$

10. $\sqrt[3]{9t^5v^8} \cdot \sqrt[3]{6tv^4}$

11. $\sqrt{60} \cdot \sqrt{105}$

12. $\sqrt[3]{3600} \cdot \sqrt[3]{165}$

13. $\sqrt{810} + \sqrt{240} + \sqrt{135} - \sqrt{250}$

14. $\sqrt[3]{216} - \sqrt[3]{48} + \sqrt[3]{432}$

15. $(\sqrt{12} - 2\sqrt{3})^2$

16. $(\sqrt{18} + 2\sqrt{3})^2$

17. $(\sqrt{5} - \sqrt{6})(\sqrt{5} + \sqrt{2})$

18. $(\sqrt{50} + \sqrt{27})(\sqrt{2} - \sqrt{6})$

19. $\dfrac{3}{2 - \sqrt{5}}$

20. $\dfrac{6}{\sqrt{2} - 1}$

21. $\dfrac{5 + \sqrt{3}}{4 + \sqrt{3}}$

22. $\dfrac{6}{2 - \sqrt{7}}$

23. $\sqrt[3]{144} + \sqrt[3]{\dfrac{2}{3}} - 5\sqrt[3]{18}$

24. $\sqrt{\dfrac{3}{8}} + \sqrt{54} - \sqrt{6}$

Practice

Radical Expressions

Simplify.

1. $\sqrt[3]{-432}$ $-6\sqrt[3]{2}$

2. $\sqrt{540}$ $6\sqrt{15}$

3. $\sqrt{5}(\sqrt{10} - \sqrt{45})$ $5\sqrt{2} - 15$

4. $\sqrt[3]{6}(4\sqrt[3]{12} + 5\sqrt[3]{9})$ $8\sqrt[3]{9} + 15\sqrt[3]{2}$

5. $(2\sqrt[3]{24})(7\sqrt[3]{18})$ $84\sqrt[3]{2}$

6. $\sqrt[4]{\dfrac{8}{9a^3}}$ $\dfrac{\sqrt[4]{72a}}{3a}$

7. $\sqrt{\dfrac{11}{9}}$ $\dfrac{\sqrt{11}}{3}$

8. $\sqrt[3]{-6750}$ $-15\sqrt[3]{2}$

9. $\sqrt{3x^2y^3} \cdot \sqrt{75xy^5}$ $15|x|y^4\sqrt{x}$

10. $\sqrt[3]{9t^5v^8} \cdot \sqrt[3]{6tv^4}$ $3t^2v^4\sqrt[3]{2}$

11. $\sqrt{60} \cdot \sqrt{105}$ $30\sqrt{7}$

12. $\sqrt[3]{3600} \cdot \sqrt[3]{165}$ $30\sqrt[3]{22}$

13. $\sqrt{810} + \sqrt{240} + \sqrt{135} - \sqrt{250}$
$4\sqrt{10} + 7\sqrt{15}$

14. $\sqrt[3]{216} - \sqrt[3]{48} + \sqrt[3]{432}$
$6 - 2\sqrt[3]{6} + 6\sqrt[3]{2}$

15. $(\sqrt{12} - 2\sqrt{3})^2$ 0

16. $(\sqrt{18} + 2\sqrt{3})^2$ $30 + 12\sqrt{6}$

17. $(\sqrt{5} - \sqrt{6})(\sqrt{5} + \sqrt{2})$
$5 + \sqrt{10} - \sqrt{30} - 2\sqrt{3}$

18. $(\sqrt{50} + \sqrt{27})(\sqrt{2} - \sqrt{6})$
$10 - 10\sqrt{3} + 3\sqrt{6} - 9\sqrt{2}$

19. $\dfrac{3}{2 - \sqrt{5}}$ $-6 - 3\sqrt{5}$

20. $\dfrac{6}{\sqrt{2} - 1}$ $6\sqrt{2} + 6$

21. $\dfrac{5 + \sqrt{3}}{4 + \sqrt{3}}$ $\dfrac{17 - \sqrt{3}}{13}$

22. $\dfrac{6}{2 - \sqrt{7}}$ $-4 - 2\sqrt{7}$

23. $\sqrt[3]{144} + \sqrt[3]{\dfrac{2}{3}} - 5\sqrt[3]{18}$ $-\dfrac{8}{3}\sqrt[3]{18}$

24. $\sqrt{\dfrac{3}{8}} + \sqrt{54} - \sqrt{6}$ $\dfrac{9}{4}\sqrt{6}$

Algebra 2

Practice

Rational Exponents

Express using rational exponents.

1. $\sqrt[3]{26}$

2. $\sqrt[5]{8}$

3. $\sqrt[10]{x^6}$

4. $\sqrt[3]{28x^2y^3t^{11}}$

5. $4\sqrt{2a^{10}b^3}$

6. $\sqrt[3]{27m^6n^4}$

Simplify.

7. $x^{\frac{3}{5}}$

8. $27^{\frac{1}{6}}$

9. $a^{\frac{2}{3}}g^{\frac{1}{4}}e^{\frac{1}{2}}$

10. $w^{\frac{3}{7}}n^{\frac{5}{3}}$

11. $m^{\frac{1}{3}}v^{\frac{3}{4}}z^{\frac{5}{6}}$

12. $27^{\frac{1}{2}}b^{\frac{2}{3}}c^{\frac{7}{6}}$

13. $y^{-\frac{1}{2}}$

14. $b^{-\frac{3}{5}}$

15. $\dfrac{1}{w^{\frac{4}{5}}}$

16. $\dfrac{1}{b^{\frac{4}{7}}}$

17. $\dfrac{14}{7^{\frac{2}{3}}}$

18. $\dfrac{12}{3^{\frac{5}{2}}}$

19. $x^{-\frac{3}{5}}$

20. $\dfrac{r^2t^3}{\sqrt[4]{a^3}}$

21. $(w^{-\frac{3}{8}})^{-\frac{4}{9}}$

22. $(\sqrt[8]{11}x^{\frac{3}{4}}y^{-\frac{1}{2}})^4$

23. $\dfrac{r^{\frac{3}{4}}y^{-\frac{3}{2}}}{\sqrt{yr^{-\frac{1}{2}}}}$

24. $\left(\dfrac{n^{-\frac{4}{5}}}{x^{-10}n^{\frac{2}{5}}}\right)^{-5}$

Algebra 2

NAME _____ DATE _____

Practice

Rational Exponents

Express using rational exponents.

1. $\sqrt[3]{26}$ $26^{\frac{1}{3}}$

2. $\sqrt[5]{8}$ $8^{\frac{1}{5}}$ or $2^{\frac{3}{5}}$

3. $\sqrt[10]{x^6}$ $x^{\frac{3}{5}}$

4. $\sqrt[3]{28x^2y^3t^{11}}$ $28^{\frac{1}{3}}x^{\frac{2}{3}}yt^{\frac{11}{3}}$

5. $4\sqrt{2a^{10}b^3}$ $2^{\frac{5}{2}}a^5b^{\frac{3}{2}}$ or $4 \cdot 2^{\frac{1}{2}}a^5b^{\frac{3}{2}}$

6. $\sqrt[3]{27m^6n^4}$ $3m^2n^{\frac{4}{3}}$

Simplify.

7. $x^{\frac{3}{5}}$ $\sqrt[5]{x^3}$

8. $27^{\frac{1}{6}}$ $\sqrt{3}$

9. $a^{\frac{2}{3}}g^{\frac{1}{4}}e^{\frac{1}{2}}$ $\sqrt[12]{a^8g^3e^6}$

10. $w^{\frac{3}{7}}n^{\frac{5}{3}}$ $n\sqrt[21]{w^9n^{14}}$

11. $m^{\frac{1}{3}}v^{\frac{3}{4}}z^{\frac{5}{6}}$ $\sqrt[12]{m^4v^9z^{10}}$

12. $27^{\frac{1}{2}}b^{\frac{2}{3}}c^{\frac{7}{6}}$ $3c\sqrt[6]{27b^4c}$

13. $y^{-\frac{1}{2}}$ $\dfrac{y^{\frac{1}{2}}}{y}$

14. $b^{-\frac{3}{5}}$ $\dfrac{b^{\frac{2}{5}}}{b}$

15. $\dfrac{1}{w^{\frac{4}{5}}}$ $\dfrac{w^{\frac{1}{5}}}{w}$

16. $\dfrac{1}{b^{\frac{4}{7}}}$ $\dfrac{b^{\frac{3}{7}}}{b}$

17. $\dfrac{14}{7^{\frac{2}{3}}}$ $2 \cdot 7^{\frac{1}{3}}$

18. $\dfrac{12}{3^{\frac{5}{2}}}$ $\dfrac{4 \cdot 3^{\frac{1}{2}}}{9}$

19. $x^{-\frac{3}{5}}$ $\dfrac{x^{\frac{2}{5}}}{x}$

20. $\dfrac{r^2t^3}{\sqrt[4]{a^3}}$ $\dfrac{r^2t^3a^{\frac{1}{4}}}{a}$

21. $(w^{-\frac{3}{8}})^{-\frac{4}{9}}$ $w^{\frac{1}{6}}$

22. $(\sqrt[8]{11}x^{\frac{3}{4}}y^{-\frac{1}{2}})^4$ $\dfrac{\sqrt{11}x^3}{y^2}$

23. $\dfrac{r^{-\frac{3}{4}}y^{-\frac{3}{2}}}{\sqrt{y}r^{-\frac{1}{2}}}$ $\dfrac{r^{\frac{3}{4}}}{y^2r}$

24. $\left(\dfrac{n^{-\frac{4}{5}}}{x^{-10}n^{\frac{2}{5}}}\right)^{-5}$ $\dfrac{n^6}{x^{50}}$

Solving Equations Containing Radicals

Solve each equation. Be sure to check for extraneous solutions.

1. $7x\sqrt{3} - 5 = 0$

2. $4x - x\sqrt{3} = 6$

3. $18 - 3x = x\sqrt{2}$

4. $\sqrt{x + 8} - 5 = 0$

5. $\sqrt[3]{y - 7} = 4$

6. $\sqrt[4]{3x} - 2 = 0$

7. $\sqrt{8n - 5} - 1 = 2$

8. $\sqrt{1 - 4t} - 8 = -6$

9. $\sqrt[4]{7v - 2} + 12 = 7$

10. $\sqrt[3]{6u - 5} + 2 = -3$

11. $\sqrt{6x - 4} = \sqrt{2x + 10}$

12. $\sqrt{9u - 4} = \sqrt{7u - 20}$

13. $\sqrt{k + 9} - \sqrt{k} = \sqrt{3}$

14. $\sqrt{x + 10} + \sqrt{x - 6} = 8$

15. $\sqrt{x + 2} - 7 = \sqrt{x + 9}$

16. $\sqrt{4x^2 - 3x + 2} - 2x - 5 = 0$

Practice

Solving Equations Containing Radicals

Solve each equation. Be sure to check for extraneous solutions.

1. $7x\sqrt{3} - 5 = 0$

$\dfrac{5\sqrt{3}}{21}$

2. $4x - x\sqrt{3} = 6$

$\dfrac{24 + 6\sqrt{3}}{13}$

3. $18 - 3x = x\sqrt{2}$

$\dfrac{54 - 18\sqrt{2}}{7}$

4. $\sqrt{x + 8} - 5 = 0$

17

5. $\sqrt[3]{y - 7} = 4$

71

6. $\sqrt[4]{3x} - 2 = 0$

$\dfrac{16}{3}$

7. $\sqrt{8n - 5} - 1 = 2$

$\dfrac{7}{4}$

8. $\sqrt{1 - 4t} - 8 = -6$

$-\dfrac{3}{4}$

9. $\sqrt[4]{7v - 2} + 12 = 7$

no real solution

10. $\sqrt[3]{6u - 5} + 2 = -3$

−20

11. $\sqrt{6x - 4} = \sqrt{2x + 10}$

$\dfrac{7}{2}$

12. $\sqrt{9u - 4} = \sqrt{7u - 20}$

no real solution

13. $\sqrt{k + 9} - \sqrt{k} = \sqrt{3}$

3

14. $\sqrt{x + 10} + \sqrt{x - 6} = 8$

15

15. $\sqrt{x + 2} - 7 = \sqrt{x + 9}$

no real solution

16. $\sqrt{4x^2 - 3x + 2} - 2x - 5 = 0$

−1

Algebra 2

NAME_____ DATE _____

Practice

Complex Numbers

Simplify.

1. $\sqrt{-49}$

2. $\sqrt{-48}$

3. $6\sqrt{-12}$

4. $\sqrt{\dfrac{-16}{25}}$

5. $\sqrt{\dfrac{-2}{7}}$

6. $\sqrt{\dfrac{-8}{3}}$

7. i^{42}

8. i^{91}

9. $(7 - 6i) + (9 + 11i)$

10. $(5 + \sqrt{-8}) + (-13 + 4\sqrt{-2})$

11. $-6(2 - 8i) + 3(5 + 7i)$

12. $4(7 - i) - 5(2 - 6i)$

13. $(3 - 4i)^2$

14. $(\sqrt{5} + 2i)^2$

15. $(6 - 4i)(6 + 4i)$

16. $(8 - \sqrt{-11})(8 + \sqrt{-11})$

17. $5(2 + 3i) + 6(8 - 5i)$

18. $(4 + 3i)(2 - 5i)(4 - 3i)$

Solve each equation.

19. $n^2 + 25 = 0$

20. $m^2 + 10 = 0$

21. $6y^2 + 42 = 0$

22. $4r^2 + 64 = 0$

Find the values of x and y for which each equation is true.

23. $3x - 5yi = 15 - 20i$

24. $\sqrt{3}x + 7yi = 6 - 2i$

Algebra 2

5-9

Practice

Complex Numbers

Simplify.

1. $\sqrt{-49}$ **7i**

2. $\sqrt{-48}$ **4i$\sqrt{3}$**

3. $6\sqrt{-12}$ **12i$\sqrt{3}$**

4. $\sqrt{\dfrac{-16}{25}}$ **$\dfrac{4}{5}i$**

5. $\sqrt{\dfrac{-2}{7}}$ **$\dfrac{i\sqrt{14}}{7}$**

6. $\sqrt{\dfrac{-8}{3}}$ **$\dfrac{2i\sqrt{6}}{3}$**

7. i^{42} **−1**

8. i^{91} **−i**

9. $(7 - 6i) + (9 + 11i)$
   16 + 5i

10. $(5 + \sqrt{-8}) + (-13 + 4\sqrt{-2})$
    − 8 + 6i$\sqrt{2}$

11. $-6(2 - 8i) + 3(5 + 7i)$
    3 + 69i

12. $4(7 - i) - 5(2 - 6i)$
    18 + 26i

13. $(3 - 4i)^2$
    −7 − 24i

14. $(\sqrt{5} + 2i)^2$
    1 + 4i$\sqrt{5}$

15. $(6 - 4i)(6 + 4i)$
    52

16. $(8 - \sqrt{-11})(8 + \sqrt{-11})$
    75

17. $5(2 + 3i) + 6(8 - 5i)$
    58 − 15i

18. $(4 + 3i)(2 - 5i)(4 - 3i)$
    50 − 125i

Solve each equation.

19. $n^2 + 25 = 0$ **±5i**

20. $m^2 + 10 = 0$ **±i$\sqrt{10}$**

21. $6y^2 + 42 = 0$ **±i$\sqrt{7}$**

22. $4r^2 + 64 = 0$ **±4i**

Find the values of x and y for which each equation is true.

23. $3x - 5yi = 15 - 20i$
    x = 5
    y = 4

24. $\sqrt{3}x + 7yi = 6 - 2i$
    x = 2$\sqrt{3}$
    y = $-\dfrac{2}{7}$

5-10

Practice

Simplifying Expressions Containing Complex Numbers

Simplify.

1. $\dfrac{2 - 4i}{1 + 3i}$

2. $\dfrac{3 - i}{2 - i}$

3. $\dfrac{6 + 5i}{-2i}$

4. $\dfrac{1 + 6i}{5i}$

5. $\dfrac{3 - 6i}{-4i}$

6. $\dfrac{2 + 7i}{-5i}$

7. $\dfrac{3}{6 + 4i}$

8. $\dfrac{2}{7 - 8i}$

9. $\dfrac{3}{\sqrt{2} - 5i}$

10. $\dfrac{2 + i\sqrt{3}}{1 + i\sqrt{3}}$

11. $\dfrac{(1 - 2i)^2}{(2 - i)^2}$

12. $\dfrac{2 + i}{(1 - i)^2}$

13. $\dfrac{3}{\sqrt{5} + 2i}$

14. $\dfrac{2 - i}{\sqrt{2} + 2i}$

15. $\dfrac{(1 + 3i)^2}{(4 - i)^2}$

16. $\dfrac{2 - i\sqrt{3}}{1 + i\sqrt{3}}$

Find the multiplicative inverse of each complex number.

17. $5 + 2i$

18. $3 - i$

19. $\dfrac{i}{7 + 4i}$

20. $\dfrac{-6i}{4 - 5i}$

NAME_____ DATE _____

Practice

Student Edition
Pages 317–321

Simplifying Expressions Containing Complex Numbers

Simplify.

1. $\dfrac{2 - 4i}{1 + 3i}$ $-1 - i$

2. $\dfrac{3 - i}{2 - i}$ $\dfrac{7 + i}{5}$

3. $\dfrac{6 + 5i}{-2i}$ $\dfrac{-5 + 6i}{2}$

4. $\dfrac{1 + 6i}{5i}$ $\dfrac{6 - i}{5}$

5. $\dfrac{3 - 6i}{-4i}$ $\dfrac{6 + 3i}{4}$

6. $\dfrac{2 + 7i}{-5i}$ $\dfrac{-7 + 2i}{5}$

7. $\dfrac{3}{6 + 4i}$ $\dfrac{9 - 6i}{26}$

8. $\dfrac{2}{7 - 8i}$ $\dfrac{14 + 16i}{113}$

9. $\dfrac{3}{\sqrt{2} - 5i}$ $\dfrac{\sqrt{2} + 5i}{9}$

10. $\dfrac{2 + i\sqrt{3}}{1 + i\sqrt{3}}$ $\dfrac{5 - i\sqrt{3}}{4}$

11. $\dfrac{(1 - 2i)^2}{(2 - i)^2}$ $\dfrac{7 - 24i}{25}$

12. $\dfrac{2 + i}{(1 - i)^2}$ $\dfrac{-1 + 2i}{2}$

13. $\dfrac{3}{\sqrt{5} + 2i}$ $\dfrac{\sqrt{5} - 2i}{3}$

14. $\dfrac{2 - i}{\sqrt{2} + 2i}$ $\dfrac{-2 + 2\sqrt{2} - (4 + \sqrt{2})i}{6}$

15. $\dfrac{(1 + 3i)^2}{(4 - i)^2}$ $\dfrac{-168 + 26i}{289}$

16. $\dfrac{2 - i\sqrt{3}}{1 + i\sqrt{3}}$ $\dfrac{-1 - 3i\sqrt{3}}{4}$

Find the multiplicative inverse of each complex number.

17. $5 + 2i$ $\dfrac{5 - 2i}{29}$

18. $3 - i$ $\dfrac{3 + i}{10}$

19. $\dfrac{i}{7 + 4i}$ $4 - 7i$

20. $\dfrac{-6i}{4 - 5i}$ $\dfrac{5 + 4i}{6}$

Practice

Solving Quadratic Equations by Graphing

Identify the quadratic term, the linear term, and the constant term in each function.

1. $f(x) = x^2 + 14x + 49$

2. $f(x) = 54x^2 + 36x + 10$

3. $f(x) = -3(2x + 1)^2$

4. $f(x) = -\frac{2}{3}(x - 6)^2 + 4$

Graph each function. Name the vertex and the axis of symmetry.

5. $f(x) = x^2 - 10x + 25$

6. $f(x) = x^2 + 12x + 36$

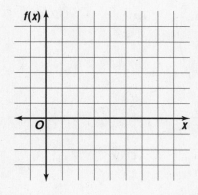
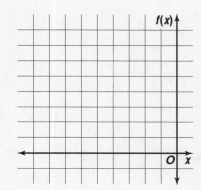

Solve each equation by graphing.

7. $y = (x + 5)^2 - 1$

8. $x^2 + 2x = 0$

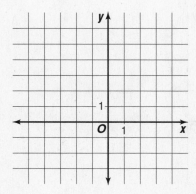
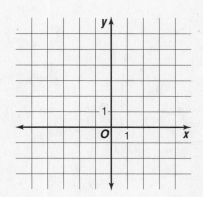

Solving Quadratic Equations by Graphing

Identify the quadratic term, the linear term, and the constant term in each function.

1. $f(x) = x^2 + 14x + 49$
   x^2; 14x; 49

2. $f(x) = 54x^2 + 36x + 10$
   $54x^2$; 36x; 10

3. $f(x) = -3(2x + 1)^2$
   $-12x^2$; −12x; −3

4. $f(x) = -\frac{2}{3}(x - 6)^2 + 4$
   $-\frac{2}{3}x^2$; 8x; −20

Graph each function. Name the vertex and the axis of symmetry.

5. $f(x) = x^2 - 10x + 25$

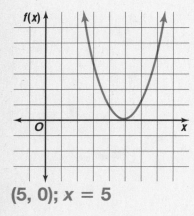

(5, 0); x = 5

6. $f(x) = x^2 + 12x + 36$

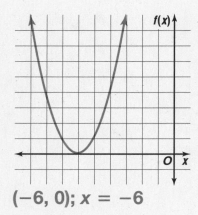

(−6, 0); x = −6

Solve each equation by graphing.

7. $y = (x + 5)^2 - 1$ **−6, −4**

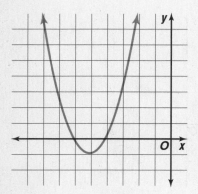

8. $x^2 + 2x = 0$ **−2, 0**

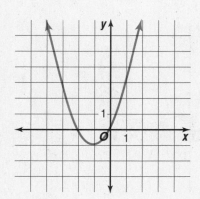

Practice

Solving Quadratic Equations by Factoring

Solve each equation by factoring.

1. $x^2 - 4x - 12 = 0$

2. $y^2 - 16y + 64 = 0$

3. $n^2 + 25 = 10n$

4. $9z = 10z^2$

5. $7y^2 = 4y$

6. $c^2 = 2c + 99$

7. $5w^2 - 35w + 60 = 0$

8. $3d^2 + 24d + 45 = 0$

9. $15v^2 + 19v + 6 = 0$

10. $4j^2 + 6 = 11j$

11. $36k^2 = 25$

12. $12m^3 - 8m^2 = 15m$

13. $6e^3 = 5e^2 + 6e$

14. $9 = 64p^2$

Solve. Use any strategy.

15. At a cattle pen at the county fair, Jody counted 65 heads and 236 legs. How many cattle and how many workers were there in the pen at that time?

16. Replace each letter with a whole number so that the addition problem at the right is correct. Each letter represents a different number. (There are four possible answers.)

$$\begin{array}{cccc} A & B & C & D \\ + D & C & B & A \\ \hline 5 & 5 & 5 & 5 \end{array}$$

Algebra 2

Practice

Solving Quadratic Equations by Factoring

Solve each equation by factoring.

1. $x^2 - 4x - 12 = 0$ **6, −2**

2. $y^2 - 16y + 64 = 0$ **8**

3. $n^2 + 25 = 10n$ **5**

4. $9z = 10z^2$ **0, $\frac{9}{10}$**

5. $7y^2 = 4y$ **0, $\frac{4}{7}$**

6. $c^2 = 2c + 99$ **−9, 11**

7. $5w^2 - 35w + 60 = 0$ **3, 4**

8. $3d^2 + 24d + 45 = 0$ **−5, −3**

9. $15v^2 + 19v + 6 = 0$ **$-\frac{3}{5}$, $-\frac{2}{3}$**

10. $4j^2 + 6 = 11j$ **$\frac{3}{4}$, 2**

11. $36k^2 = 25$ **$\frac{5}{6}$, $-\frac{5}{6}$**

12. $12m^3 - 8m^2 = 15m$ **0, $-\frac{5}{6}$, $\frac{3}{2}$**

13. $6e^3 = 5e^2 + 6e$ **0, $\frac{3}{2}$, $-\frac{2}{3}$**

14. $9 = 64p^2$ **$\frac{3}{8}$, $-\frac{3}{8}$**

Solve. Use any strategy.

15. At a cattle pen at the county fair, Jody counted 65 heads and 236 legs. How many cattle and how many workers were there in the pen at that time?
53 cattle, 12 workers

16. Replace each letter with a whole number so that the addition problem at the right is correct. Each letter represents a different number. (There are four possible answers.)
A = 1, B = 2, C = 3, D = 4;
A = 1, B = 3, C = 2, D = 4;
A = 2, B = 4, C = 1, D = 3;
A = 2, B = 1, C = 4, D = 3

$$\begin{array}{r} \text{A B C D} \\ + \text{D C B A} \\ \hline \text{5 5 5 5} \end{array}$$

Completing the Square

Find the value of c that makes each trinomial a perfect square.

1. $a^2 + 12a + c$

2. $h^2 - 20h + c$

3. $p^2 - p + c$

4. $m^2 + 11m + c$

5. $t^2 + \dfrac{5}{6}t + c$

6. $u^2 - \dfrac{u}{4} + c$

7. $b^2 - \dfrac{5}{3}b + c$

8. $x^2 + 17x + c$

Find the exact solution for each equation by completing the square.

9. $x^2 - 14x + 19 = 0$

10. $n^2 + 16n - 7 = 0$

11. $d^2 + d - 5 = 0$

12. $v^2 + 18 = 9v$

13. $3x^2 - 5x + 2 = 0$

14. $2x^2 + 8x - 3 = 0$

15. $2b^2 - 5b - 6 = 0$

16. $p^2 + 8p + 10 = 0$

17. $q^2 - 9q + 11 = 0$

18. $3a^2 + a - 2 = 0$

19. $c^2 + 6c + 8 = 0$

20. $2d^2 - 10d + 5 = 0$

NAME _____ DATE _____

Practice

Completing the Square

Find the value of c that makes each trinomial a perfect square.

1. $a^2 + 12a + c$ **36**

2. $h^2 - 20h + c$ **100**

3. $p^2 - p + c$ $\dfrac{1}{4}$

4. $m^2 + 11m + c$ $\dfrac{121}{4}$

5. $t^2 + \dfrac{5}{6}t + c$ $\dfrac{25}{144}$

6. $u^2 - \dfrac{u}{4} + c$ $\dfrac{1}{64}$

7. $b^2 - \dfrac{5}{3}b + c$ $\dfrac{25}{36}$

8. $x^2 + 17x + c$ $\dfrac{289}{4}$

Find the exact solution for each equation by completing the square.

9. $x^2 - 14x + 19 = 0$ $7 \pm \sqrt{30}$

10. $n^2 + 16n - 7 = 0$ $-8 \pm \sqrt{71}$

11. $d^2 + d - 5 = 0$ $\dfrac{-1 \pm \sqrt{21}}{2}$

12. $v^2 + 18 = 9v$ **6, 3**

13. $3x^2 - 5x + 2 = 0$ $1, \dfrac{2}{3}$

14. $2x^2 + 8x - 3 = 0$ $\dfrac{-4 \pm \sqrt{22}}{2}$

15. $2b^2 - 5b - 6 = 0$ $\dfrac{5 \pm \sqrt{73}}{4}$

16. $p^2 + 8p + 10 = 0$ $-4 \pm \sqrt{6}$

17. $q^2 - 9q + 11 = 0$ $\dfrac{9 \pm \sqrt{37}}{2}$

18. $3a^2 + a - 2 = 0$ $\dfrac{2}{3}, -1$

19. $c^2 + 6c + 8 = 0$ $-4, -2$

20. $2d^2 - 10d + 5 = 0$ $\dfrac{5 \pm \sqrt{15}}{2}$

Algebra 2

Practice

The Quadratic Formula and the Discriminant

Find the value of the discriminant and describe the nature of the roots of each quadratic equation. Then solve the equation. Express irrational roots as exact and approximate to the nearest hundredth.

1. $x^2 - 9x + 14 = 0$

2. $r^2 = 3r$

3. $9u^2 - 24u + 16 = 0$

4. $n^2 - 3n = 40$

5. $3t^2 + 9t - 2 = 0$

6. $7u^2 + 6u + 2 = 0$

7. $5w^2 - 2w + 4 = 0$

8. $12x^2 - x - 6 = 0$

9. $2m^2 + 7m = 0$

10. $x^2 - \frac{1}{2}x + \frac{1}{16} = 0$

11. $12x^2 + 2x - 4 = 0$

12. $6w^2 - 2w - 1 = 0$

Practice

The Quadratic Formula and the Discriminant

Find the value of the discriminant and describe the nature of the roots of each quadratic equation. Then solve the equation. Express irrational roots as exact and approximate to the nearest hundredth.

1. $x^2 - 9x + 14 = 0$
   25; 2 real, rational; 7, 2

2. $r^2 = 3r$
   9; 2 real, rational; 0, 3

3. $9u^2 - 24u + 16 = 0$
   0; 1 real, rational; $\frac{4}{3}$

4. $n^2 - 3n = 40$
   169; 2 real, rational; −5, 8

5. $3t^2 + 9t - 2 = 0$
   105; 2 real, irrational; $\frac{-9 \pm \sqrt{105}}{6}$;
   0.21, −3.21

6. $7u^2 + 6u + 2 = 0$
   −20; 2 imaginary; $\frac{-3 \pm \sqrt{5}i}{7}$

7. $5w^2 - 2w + 4 = 0$
   −76; 2 imaginary; $\frac{1 \pm \sqrt{19}i}{5}$

8. $12x^2 - x - 6 = 0$
   289; 2 real, rational; $\frac{3}{4}$, $-\frac{2}{3}$

9. $2m^2 + 7m = 0$
   49; 2 real, rational; 0, $-\frac{7}{2}$

10. $x^2 - \frac{1}{2}x + \frac{1}{16} = 0$
    0; 1 real, rational; $\frac{1}{4}$

11. $12x^2 + 2x - 4 = 0$
    196; 2 real, rational; $\frac{1}{2}$, $-\frac{2}{3}$

12. $6w^2 - 2w - 1 = 0$
    28; 2 real, irrational; $\frac{1 \pm \sqrt{7}}{6}$;
    0.61, −0.27

Algebra 2

Practice

Sum and Product of Roots

Solve each equation. Then find the sum and the product of the roots to check your solutions.

1. $x^2 - 7x + 4 = 0$

2. $x^2 + 3x + 6 = 0$

3. $2n^2 + 5n + 6 = 0$

4. $7x^2 - 5x = 0$

5. $4r^2 - 9 = 0$

6. $-5x^2 - x + 4 = 0$

7. $3x^2 + 8x = 3$

8. $\frac{2}{3}x^2 - \frac{1}{2}x - 1 = 0$

Write a quadratic equation that has the given roots.

9. $7, -3$

10. $4, \frac{1}{3}$

11. $-\frac{2}{3}, -\frac{4}{5}$

12. $-2\sqrt{5}, 4\sqrt{5}$

13. $3 - \sqrt{6}, 3 + \sqrt{6}$

14. $7 - 2i, 7 + 2i$

15. $7i, -7i$

16. $\frac{2 + \sqrt{10}}{5}, \frac{2 - \sqrt{10}}{5}$

17. $2 + i\sqrt{11}, 2 - i\sqrt{11}$

18. $\frac{1 + 6i}{4}, \frac{1 - 6i}{4}$

Find k such that the number given is a root of the equation.

19. $7; 2x^2 + kx - 21 = 0$

20. $-2; x^2 - 13x + k = 0$

Practice

Sum and Product of Roots

Solve each equation. Then find the sum and the product of the roots to check your solutions.

1. $x^2 - 7x + 4 = 0$ $\dfrac{7 \pm \sqrt{33}}{2}$; 7; 4

2. $x^2 + 3x + 6 = 0$ $\dfrac{-3 \pm \sqrt{15}i}{2}$; $-3, 6$

3. $2n^2 + 5n + 6 = 0$ $\dfrac{-5 \pm \sqrt{23}i}{4}$; $-\dfrac{5}{3}$; 3

4. $7x^2 - 5x = 0$ $0, \dfrac{5}{7}$; $\dfrac{5}{7}$; 0

5. $4r^2 - 9 = 0$ $\dfrac{3}{2}, -\dfrac{3}{2}$; 0; $-\dfrac{9}{4}$

6. $-5x^2 - x + 4 = 0$ $-1, \dfrac{4}{5}$; $-\dfrac{1}{5}$; $-\dfrac{4}{5}$

7. $3x^2 + 8x = 3$ $\dfrac{1}{3}, -3$; $-\dfrac{8}{3}$; -1

8. $\dfrac{2}{3}x^2 - \dfrac{1}{2}x - 1 = 0$ $\dfrac{3 \pm \sqrt{105}}{8}$; $\dfrac{3}{4}$; $-\dfrac{3}{2}$

Write a quadratic equation that has the given roots.

9. $7, -3$ $x^2 - 4x - 21 = 0$

10. $4, \dfrac{1}{3}$ $3x^2 - 13x + 4 = 0$

11. $-\dfrac{2}{3}, -\dfrac{4}{5}$ $15x^2 + 22x + 8 = 0$

12. $-2\sqrt{5}, 4\sqrt{5}$ $x^2 - 2\sqrt{5}x - 40 = 0$

13. $3 - \sqrt{6}, 3 + \sqrt{6}$ $x^2 - 6x + 3 = 0$

14. $7 - 2i, 7 + 2i$ $x^2 - 14x + 53 = 0$

15. $7i, -7i$ $x^2 + 49 = 0$

16. $\dfrac{2 + \sqrt{10}}{5}, \dfrac{2 - \sqrt{10}}{5}$

$25x^2 - 20x - 6 = 0$

17. $2 + i\sqrt{11}, 2 - i\sqrt{11}$

$x^2 - 4x + 15 = 0$

18. $\dfrac{1 + 6i}{4}, \dfrac{1 - 6i}{4}$ $16x^2 - 8x + 37 = 0$

Find k such that the number given is a root of the equation.

19. $7; 2x^2 + kx - 21 = 0$ -11

20. $-2; x^2 - 13x + k = 0$ -30

NAME_____ DATE _____

Practice

Analyzing Graphs of Quadratic Functions

Write each equation in the form $f(x) = a(x - h)^2 + k$. Then name the vertex, axis of symmetry, and direction of opening for the graph of each quadratic function.

1. $f(x) = -6x^2$

2. $y = -2x^2 - 16x - 32$

3. $h(x) = \frac{2}{3}x^2 + 4x + 6$

4. $y = 2x^2 + 16x + 29$

5. $g(x) = -9x^2 + 12x - 4$

6. $y = -3x^2 + 6x - 5$

Write the equation of the parabola that passes through the given points.

7. $(0, 1), (2, -1), (1, 3)$

8. $(0, 0), (2, 3), (-1, 4)$

Graph each function.

9. $f(x) = -2x^2 + 1$

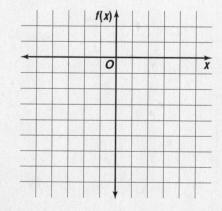

10. $f(x) = -3x^2 + 6x - 5$

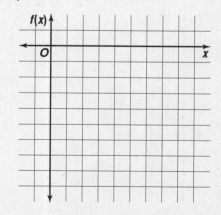

Algebra 2

NAME _____ DATE _____

Practice

Analyzing Graphs of Quadratic Functions

Write each equation in the form $f(x) = a(x - h)^2 + k$. Then name the vertex, axis of symmetry, and direction of opening for the graph of each quadratic function.

1. $f(x) = -6x^2$
$f(x) = -6x^2$; $(0, 0)$;
$x = 0$; down

2. $y = -2x^2 - 16x - 32$
$f(x) = -2(x + 4)^2$; $(-4, 0)$;
$x = -4$; down

3. $h(x) = \frac{2}{3}x^2 + 4x + 6$
$f(x) = \frac{2}{3}(x + 3)^2$; $(-3, 0)$;
$x = -3$; up

4. $y = 2x^2 + 16x + 29$
$f(x) = 2(x + 4)^2 - 3$;
$(-4, -3)$; $x = -4$; up

5. $g(x) = -9x^2 + 12x - 4$
$g(x) = -9\left(x - \frac{2}{3}\right)^2$; $\left(\frac{2}{3}, 0\right)$;
$x = \frac{2}{3}$; down

6. $y = -3x^2 + 6x - 5$
$f(x) = -3(x - 1)^2 - 2$;
$(1, -2)$; $x = 1$; down

Write the equation of the parabola that passes through the given points.

7. $(0, 1), (2, -1), (1, 3)$
$f(x) = -3x^2 + 5x + 1$

8. $(0, 0), (2, 3), (-1, 4)$
$f(x) = \frac{11}{6}x^2 - \frac{13}{6}x$

Graph each function.

9. $f(x) = -2x^2 + 1$

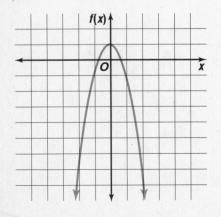

10. $f(x) = -3x^2 + 6x - 5$

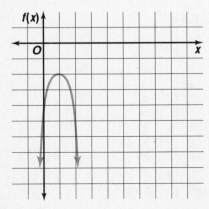

Algebra 2

Practice

Graphing and Solving Quadratic Inequalities

Graph each inequality.

1. $y \le x^2 + 4$

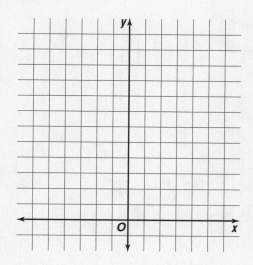

2. $y < x^2 + 8x - 5$

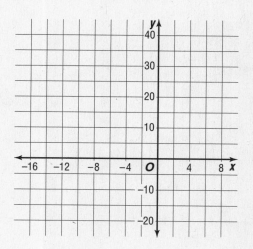

Solve each inequality.

3. $x^2 - x - 20 > 0$

4. $x^2 - 10x + 16 < 0$

5. $5x^2 + 10 \ge 27x$

6. $9x^2 + 31x + 12 \le 0$

7. $9z \le 12z^2$

8. $4x^2 + 4x + 1 > 0$

9. $x^2 + 64 \ge 16x$

10. $x^2 + \frac{4}{3}x + \frac{4}{9} < 0$

11. $9x^2 + 6x + 1 \le 0$

12. $2x^2 + 3 \le 8x$

Graphing and Solving Quadratic Inequalities

Graph each inequality.

1. $y \leq x^2 + 4$

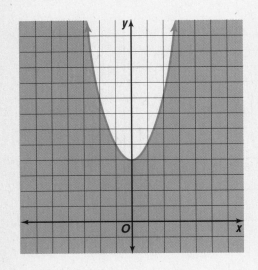

2. $y < x^2 + 8x - 5$

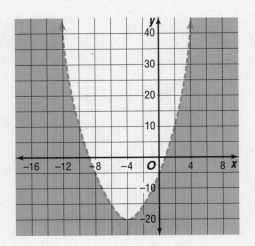

Solve each inequality.

3. $x^2 - x - 20 > 0$
$\{x|x > 5 \text{ or } x < -4\}$

4. $x^2 - 10x + 16 < 0$
$\{x|2 < x < 8\}$

5. $5x^2 + 10 \geq 27x$
$\left\{x|x \geq 5 \text{ or } x \leq \frac{2}{5}\right\}$

6. $9x^2 + 31x + 12 \leq 0$
$\left\{x|-3 \leq x \leq -\frac{4}{9}\right\}$

7. $9z \leq 12z^2$
$\left\{z|z \geq \frac{3}{4} \text{ or } z \leq 0\right\}$

8. $4x^2 + 4x + 1 > 0$
$\left\{x|x \neq -\frac{1}{2}\right\}$

9. $x^2 + 64 \geq 16x$
all reals

10. $x^2 + \frac{4}{3}x + \frac{4}{9} < 0$
no solution

11. $9x^2 + 6x + 1 \leq 0$
$\left\{-\frac{1}{3}\right\}$

12. $2x^2 + 3 \leq 8x$
$\left\{x|\frac{4 - \sqrt{10}}{2} \leq x \leq \frac{4 + \sqrt{10}}{2}\right\}$

Practice

Integration: Statistics
Standard Deviation

Find the mean and standard deviation to the nearest hundredth for each set of data.

1. {3, 5, 2, 6, 5, 9, 5, 2, 8, 6}

2. {6.1, 2.5, 4.8, 3.8, 7.1, 6.1, 5.9}

3. {0.050, 0.048, 0.051, 0.047, 0.048, 0.053, 0.044, 0.048, 0.052, 0.046}

4. {26, 37, 89, 42, 56, 43, 27, 18, 72, 83}

5. {156, 283, 102, 127, 136, 145, 154, 129, 110, 152, 181, 193}

6. {1246, 8492, 5673, 1491, 2467, 4531, 3798, 1288, 4543, 5896}

7.
Stem	Leaf		
2	5	6	8
3	0	4	
5	3	8	
7	2		
9	4	7	9

8.
Stem	Leaf		
2	00	46	
3	23	79	86
4	51	80	
5	32	49	97

9.
Stem	Leaf			
42	1	3	7	9
48	2	4		
50	9			
52	0	3	5	

10.
Stem	Leaf		
11	00	23	59
12	27	63	
13	42	57	
14	14	98	99

Algebra 2

Integration: Statistics
Standard Deviation

Find the mean and standard deviation to the nearest hundredth for each set of data.

Accept answers reasonably close to those given here. Slight variations can result from differences in calculator models.

1. {3, 5, 2, 6, 5, 9, 5, 2, 8, 6} **5.1, 2.21**

2. {6.1, 2.5, 4.8, 3.8, 7.1, 6.1, 5.9} **5.19, 1.47**

3. {0.050, 0.048, 0.051, 0.047, 0.048, 0.053, 0.044, 0.048, 0.052, 0.046} **0.05, 0.002950**

4. {26, 37, 89, 42, 56, 43, 27, 18, 72, 83} **49.3, 23.53**

5. {156, 283, 102, 127, 136, 145, 154, 129, 110, 152, 181, 193} **155.67, 45.88**

6. {1246, 8492, 5673, 1491, 2467, 4531, 3798, 1288, 4543, 5896} **3942.5, 2252.58**

7.

Stem	Leaf
2	5 6 8
3	0 4
5	3 8
7	2
9	4 7 9

56, 28.68

8.

Stem	Leaf
2	00 46
3	23 79 86
4	51 80
5	32 49 97

414.3, 124.77

9.

Stem	Leaf
42	1 3 7 9
48	2 4
50	9
52	0 3 5

474.3, 42.60

10.

Stem	Leaf
11	00 23 59
12	27 63
13	42 57
14	14 98 99

1298.2, 139.53

Practice

Integration: Statistics
The Normal Distribution

The weights of eggs produced on a farm are normally distributed with a mean of 1.4 ounces and a standard deviation of 0.4 ounces.

1. What percent of the eggs weigh at least 1 ounce?

2. How many of 1200 eggs are within 2 standard deviations of the mean?

3. To be graded extra large, an egg must weigh at least 2.2 ounces. What is the probability that an egg from this farm will be graded extra large?

A bottle of fruit punch must contain at least 16 fluid ounces. The machine that fills the bottles is set so that the mean volume is 16.4 fluid ounces. The volumes in the bottles are normally distributed.

4. What percent of the bottles are underfilled if the standard deviation is 0.2 fluid ounces?

5. What percent of the bottles are underfilled if the standard deviation is 0.4 fluid ounces?

6. If the standard deviation is 0.2 fluid ounces, find the mean volume that will ensure only 0.5% of the bottles will be underfilled.

A battery has an average life span of 50 hours, with a standard deviation of 3 hours. The life span of the batteries is normally distributed.

7. What percent of the batteries last at least 44 hours?

8. How many of 1500 batteries are within 1 standard deviation of the mean?

9. What percent of the batteries will last at least 53 hours?

Practice

Integration: Statistics
The Normal Distribution

The weights of eggs produced on a farm are normally distributed with a mean of 1.4 ounces and a standard deviation of 0.4 ounces.

1. What percent of the eggs weigh at least 1 ounce? **84%**

2. How many of 1200 eggs are within 2 standard deviations of the mean? **1140 eggs**

3. To be graded extra large, an egg must weigh at least 2.2 ounces. What is the probability that an egg from this farm will be graded extra large? **0.025**

A bottle of fruit punch must contain at least 16 fluid ounces. The machine that fills the bottles is set so that the mean volume is 16.4 fluid ounces. The volumes in the bottles are normally distributed.

4. What percent of the bottles are underfilled if the standard deviation is 0.2 fluid ounces? **2.5%**

5. What percent of the bottles are underfilled if the standard deviation is 0.4 fluid ounces? **16%**

6. If the standard deviation is 0.2 fluid ounces, find the mean volume that will ensure only 0.5% of the bottles will be underfilled. **16.6 fluid ounces**

A battery has an average life span of 50 hours, with a standard deviation of 3 hours. The life span of the batteries is normally distributed.

7. What percent of the batteries last at least 44 hours? **97.5%**

8. How many of 1500 batteries are within 1 standard deviation of the mean? **1020 batteries**

9. What percent of the batteries will last at least 53 hours? **16%**

Integration: Geometry
The Distance and Midpoint Formulas

Find the distance between each pair of points with the given coordinates.

1. $(-3, 5), (2, 8)$

2. $(6, -1), (-3, -2)$

3. $\left(\frac{2}{5}, 3\right), \left(\frac{3}{4}, \frac{5}{2}\right)$

4. $(-4\sqrt{2}, -\sqrt{8}), (-5\sqrt{2}, \sqrt{18})$

5. $(3\sqrt{5}, 4\sqrt{2}), (-2\sqrt{5}, 3\sqrt{8})$

6. $\left(\frac{1}{2}, \frac{2}{3}\right), \left(\frac{4}{5}, \frac{9}{10}\right)$

Find the value of c such that the distance between points with the given coordinates is 5 units.

7. $(5, 2), (c, -3)$

8. $(-2, c), (2, -1)$

9. $(0, c), (3, 1)$

10. $(c, 0), (-4, 1)$

Find the midpoint of each line segment if the coordinates of the endpoints are given.

11. $(8, -3), (-6, -11)$

12. $(-14, 5), (10, 6)$

13. $\left(-\frac{1}{2}, \sqrt{27}\right), (3, 5\sqrt{3})$

14. $(1.3, -0.6), (4, -8)$

15. $(2.6, -4.7), (8.4, 2.5)$

16. $(5, 8\sqrt{6}), (9, -2\sqrt{24})$

Integration: Geometry
The Distance and Midpoint Formulas

Find the distance between each pair of points with the given coordinates.

1. $(-3, 5), (2, 8)$ $\sqrt{34}$

2. $(6, -1), (-3, -2)$ $\sqrt{82}$

3. $\left(\frac{2}{5}, 3\right), \left(\frac{3}{4}, \frac{5}{2}\right)$ $\frac{\sqrt{149}}{20}$

4. $(-4\sqrt{2}, -\sqrt{8}), (-5\sqrt{2}, \sqrt{18})$ $2\sqrt{13}$

5. $(3\sqrt{5}, 4\sqrt{2}), (-2\sqrt{5}, 3\sqrt{8})$ $\sqrt{133}$

6. $\left(\frac{1}{2}, \frac{2}{3}\right), \left(\frac{4}{5}, \frac{9}{10}\right)$ $\frac{\sqrt{130}}{30}$

Find the value of c such that the distance between points with the given coordinates is 5 units.

7. $(5, 2), (c, -3)$ **5**

8. $(-2, c), (2, -1)$ **−4 or 2**

9. $(0, c), (3, 1)$ **−3 or 5**

10. $(c, 0), (-4, 1)$
$-4 + 2\sqrt{6}$ or $-4 - 2\sqrt{6}$

Find the midpoint of each line segment if the coordinates of the endpoints are given.

11. $(8, -3), (-6, -11)$
(1, −7)

12. $(-14, 5), (10, 6)$
$\left(-2, \frac{11}{2}\right)$

13. $\left(-\frac{1}{2}, \sqrt{27}\right), (3, 5\sqrt{3})$
$\left(\frac{5}{4}, 4\sqrt{3}\right)$

14. $(1.3, -0.6), (4, -8)$
(2.65, −4.3)

15. $(2.6, -4.7), (8.4, 2.5)$
(5.5, −1.1)

16. $(5, 8\sqrt{6}), (9, -2\sqrt{24})$
(7, 2√6)

Parabolas

Name the coordinates of the vertex and focus, the equations of the axis of symmetry and directrix, and the direction of opening of the parabola with the given equation. Then find the length of the latus rectum and graph the parabola.

1. $y = 5(x - 3)^2 + 2$

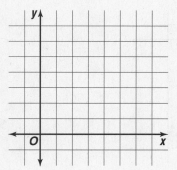

2. $y = -3(x + 1)^2 - 4$

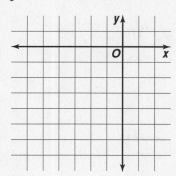

The coordinates of the focus and equation of the directrix of a parabola are given. Write an equation for each parabola. Then draw the graph.

3. $(3, 2)$, $x = -1$

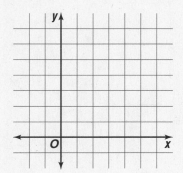

4. $(4, 1)$, $y = 3$

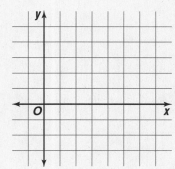

Write the equation of each parabola described below. Then draw the graph.

5. vertex, $(4, 1)$; focus, $(4, 3)$

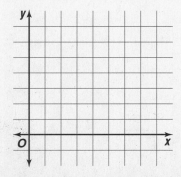

6. vertex, $(1, 2)$; focus, $(6, 2)$

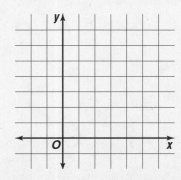

Parabolas

*Name the coordinates of the vertex and focus, the equations
of the axis of symmetry and directrix, and the direction of
opening of the parabola with the given equation. Then find
the length of the latus rectum and graph the parabola.*

1. $y = 5(x - 3)^2 + 2$ (3, 2); $\left(3, 2\frac{1}{20}\right)$; $x = 3$; $y = 1\frac{19}{20}$; up; $\frac{1}{5}$

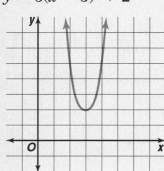

2. $y = -3(x + 1)^2 - 4$ (-1, -4); $\left(-1, -4\frac{1}{12}\right)$; $x = -1$; $y = -3\frac{11}{12}$; down; $\frac{1}{3}$

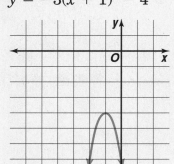
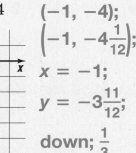

*The coordinates of the focus and equation of the directrix of
a parabola are given. Write an equation for each parabola.
Then draw the graph.*

3. (3, 2), $x = -1$ $x = \frac{1}{8}(y - 2)^2 + 1$

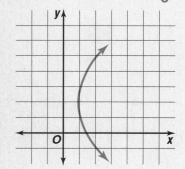

4. (4, 1), $y = 3$ $y = -\frac{1}{4}(x - 4)^2 + 2$

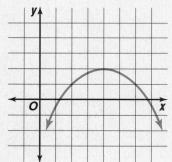

*Write the equation of each parabola described below. Then draw
the graph.*

5. vertex, (4, 1); focus, (4, 3) $y = \frac{1}{8}(x - 4)^2 + 1$

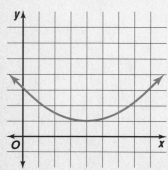

6. vertex, (1, 2); focus, (6, 2) $x = \frac{1}{20}(y - 2)^2 + 1$

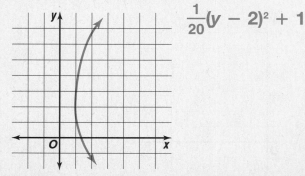

Circles

Find the coordinates of the center and the radius of each circle whose equation is given. Then draw the graph.

1. $(x + 3)^2 + y^2 = 16$

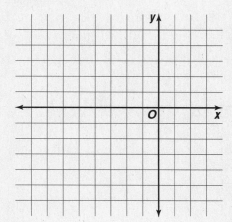

2. $3x^2 + 3y^2 = 12$

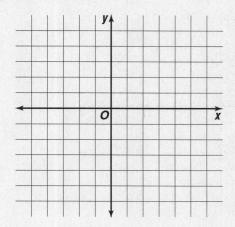

3. $x^2 + y^2 - 6x - 12y + 36 = 0$

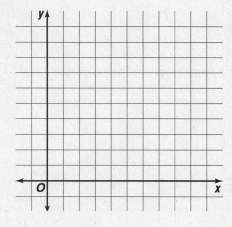

4. $x^2 + y^2 + 2x + 6y = 26$

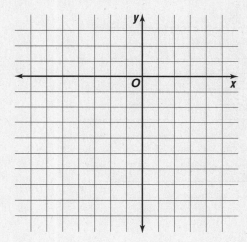

Write an equation for each circle if the coordinates of the center and length of the radius are given.

5. center $(-4, 2)$; radius 8

6. center $(5, -6)$; radius 11

7. center $\left(-\frac{1}{4}, -\sqrt{3}\right)$; radius $5\sqrt{2}$

8. center $\left(3.8, 1\frac{1}{3}\right)$; radius $\frac{3}{7}$

Practice

Circles

Find the coordinates of the center and the radius of each circle whose equation is given. Then draw the graph.

1. $(x + 3)^2 + y^2 = 16$ **(−3, 0); 4**

2. $3x^2 + 3y^2 = 12$ **(0, 0); 2**

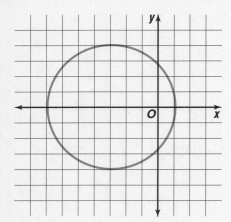

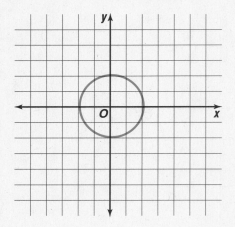

3. $x^2 + y^2 - 6x - 12y + 36 = 0$ **(3, 6); 3**

4. $x^2 + y^2 + 2x + 6y = 26$ **(−1, −3); 6**

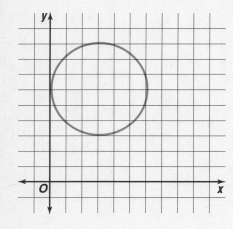

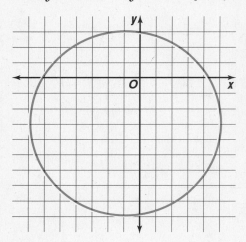

Write an equation for each circle if the coordinates of the center and length of the radius are given.

5. center (−4, 2); radius 8
   $(x + 4)^2 + (y - 2)^2 = 64$

6. center (5, −6); radius 11
   $(x - 5)^2 + (y + 6)^2 = 121$

7. center $\left(-\frac{1}{4}, -\sqrt{3}\right)$; radius $5\sqrt{2}$
   $\left(x + \frac{1}{4}\right)^2 + (y + \sqrt{3})^2 = 50$

8. center $\left(3.8, 1\frac{1}{3}\right)$; radius $\frac{3}{7}$
   $(x - 3.8)^2 + \left(y - 1\frac{1}{3}\right)^2 = \frac{9}{49}$

NAME_____ DATE _____

Practice

Ellipses

Find the coordinates of the center and foci, and lengths of the major and minor axes for each ellipse whose equation is given. Then draw the graph.

1. $\dfrac{x^2}{9} + \dfrac{y^2}{16} = 1$

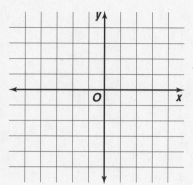

2. $16x^2 + y^2 = 64$

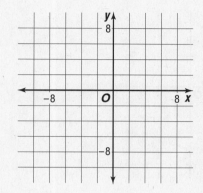

3. $\dfrac{(x-3)^2}{1} + \dfrac{(y-1)^2}{36} = 1$

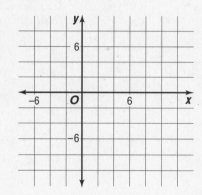

4. $\dfrac{(x+4)^2}{49} + \dfrac{(y+3)^2}{25} = 1$ **(−4, −3);**

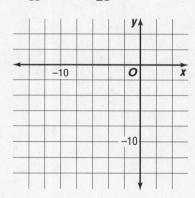

Write the equation for each ellipse described below.

5. The foci are at (4, 0) and (−4, 0). Then endpoints of the minor axis are at (0, 2) and (0, −2).

6. The center has coordinates (2, −4). The minor axis is parallel to the x-axis with a length of 6. The major axis has a length of 10.

NAME _____ DATE _____

Practice

Ellipses

*Find the coordinates of the center and foci, and lengths
of the major and minor axes for each ellipse whose equation
is given. Then draw the graph.*

1. $\frac{x^2}{9} + \frac{y^2}{16} = 1$ **(0, 0); (0, ±$\sqrt{7}$);**
8; 6

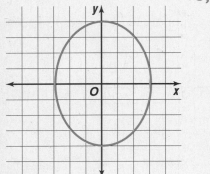

2. $16x^2 + y^2 = 64$ **(0, 0); (0, ±2$\sqrt{15}$);**
16; 4

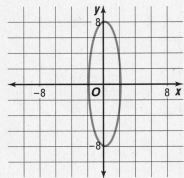

3. $\frac{(x-3)^2}{1} + \frac{(y-1)^2}{36} = 1$ **(3, 1);**
(3, 1 ±$\sqrt{35}$);
12; 2

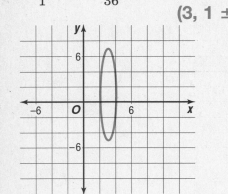

4. $\frac{(x+4)^2}{49} + \frac{(y+3)^2}{25} = 1$ **(−4, −3);**
(−4 ± 2$\sqrt{6}$, −3);
14; 10

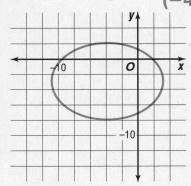

Write the equation for each ellipse described below.

5. The foci are at (4, 0) and (−4, 0). Then endpoints of the minor
axis are at (0, 2) and (0, −2).

$\frac{x^2}{20} + \frac{y^2}{4} = 1$

6. The center has coordinates (2, −4). The minor axis is parallel to
the *x*-axis with a length of 6. The major axis has a length of 10.

$\frac{(x-2)^2}{9} + \frac{(y+4)^2}{25} = 1$

Algebra 2

7-5

Practice

Hyperbolas

Find the coordinates of the vertices and foci and the slopes of the asymptotes for each hyperbola whose equation is given. Then draw the graph.

1. $\dfrac{y^2}{9} - \dfrac{x^2}{36} = 1$

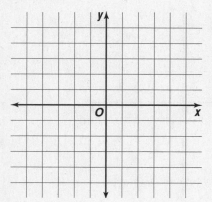

2. $y^2 - 4x^2 = 16$

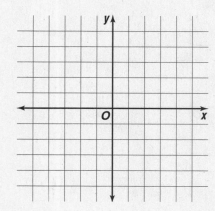

3. $\dfrac{(y-2)^2}{9} - \dfrac{(x+3)^2}{25} = 1$

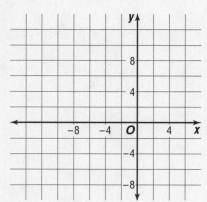

4. $\dfrac{(x-1)^2}{64} - \dfrac{(y+4)^2}{16} = 1$

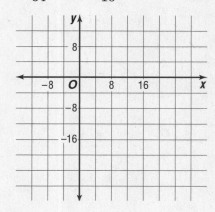

5. $4y^2 - x^2 - 16y + 2x + 11 = 0$

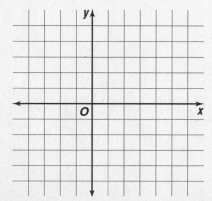

6. $3y^2 - 4x^2 + 12y + 24x = 36$

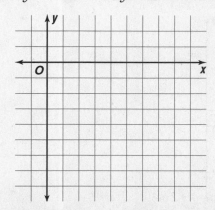

Hyperbolas

Find the coordinates of the vertices and foci and the slopes of the asymptotes for each hyperbola whose equation is given. Then draw the graph.

1. $\dfrac{y^2}{9} - \dfrac{x^2}{36} = 1$ $(0, \pm 3)$; $(0, \pm 3\sqrt{5})$; $\pm\dfrac{1}{2}$

2. $y^2 - 4x^2 = 16$ $(0, \pm 4)$; $(0, \pm 2\sqrt{5})$; ± 2

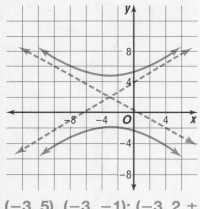

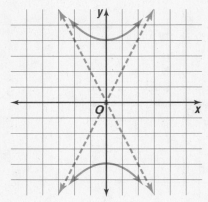

3. $\dfrac{(y-2)^2}{9} - \dfrac{(x+3)^2}{25} = 1$

4. $\dfrac{(x-1)^2}{64} - \dfrac{(y+4)^2}{16} = 1$

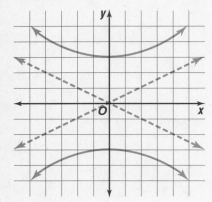

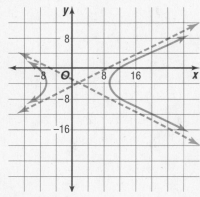

$(-3, 5), (-3, -1)$; $(-3, 2 \pm \sqrt{34})$; $\pm\dfrac{3}{5}$

$(9, -4), (-7, -4)$; $(1 \pm 4\sqrt{5}, -4)$; $\pm\dfrac{1}{2}$

5. $4y^2 - x^2 - 16y + 2x + 11 = 0$

6. $3y^2 - 4x^2 + 12y + 24x = 36$

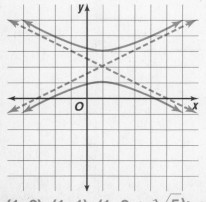

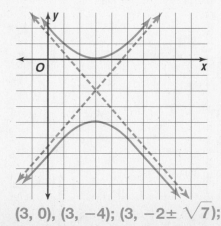

$(1, 3), (1, 1)$; $(1, 2 \pm \sqrt{5})$; $\pm\dfrac{1}{2}$

$(3, 0), (3, -4)$; $(3, -2\pm \sqrt{7})$; $\pm\dfrac{2\sqrt{3}}{3}$

NAME_____ DATE _____

Practice

Conic Sections

Write each equation in standard form. State whether the graph of the equation is a parabola, a circle, an ellipse, or a hyperbola. Then graph the equation.

1. $y^2 = -3x$

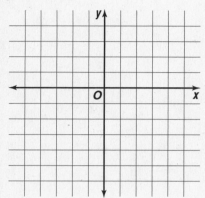

2. $x^2 + y^2 + 6x = 7$

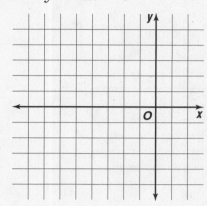

3. $5x^2 - 6y^2 - 30x - 12y + 9 = 0$

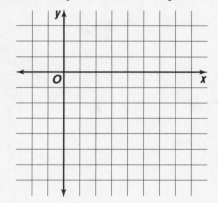

4. $3x^2 = 8 - 4y^2 - 8y$

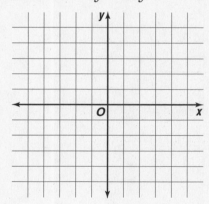

5. $5y^2 = 10 - 4x^2$

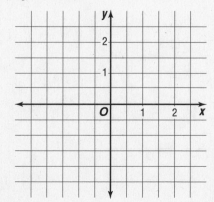

6. $5x^2 + 2y^2 + 30x - 16y + 67 = 0$

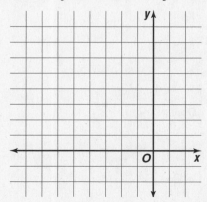

Algebra 2

Conic Sections

Write each equation in standard form. State whether the graph of the equation is a parabola, a circle, an ellipse, or a hyperbola. Then graph the equation.

1. $y^2 = -3x$

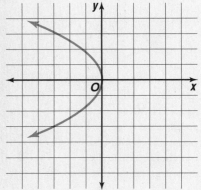

$x = -\dfrac{1}{3}(y - 0)^2 + 0$; parabola

2. $x^2 + y^2 + 6x = 7$

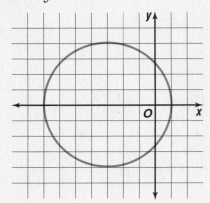

$(x + 3)^2 + (y - 0)^2 = 16$; circle

3. $5x^2 - 6y^2 - 30x - 12y + 9 = 0$

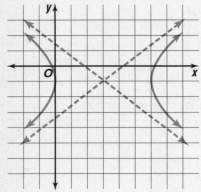

$\dfrac{(x - 3)^2}{6} - \dfrac{(y + 1)^2}{5} = 1$; hyperbola

4. $3x^2 = 8 - 4y^2 - 8y$

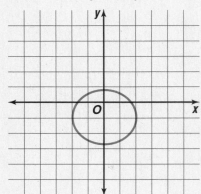

$\dfrac{(x - 0)^2}{4} + \dfrac{(y + 1)^2}{3} = 1$; ellipse

5. $5y^2 = 10 - 4x^2$

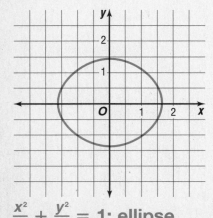

$\dfrac{x^2}{\frac{5}{2}} + \dfrac{y^2}{2} = 1$; ellipse

6. $5x^2 + 2y^2 + 30x - 16y + 67 = 0$

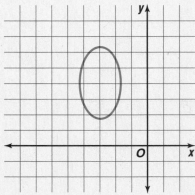

$\dfrac{(x + 3)^2}{2} + \dfrac{(y - 4)^2}{5} = 1$; ellipse

Solving Quadratic Systems

Solve each system of equations.

1. $(x - 2)^2 + y^2 = 5$
$x - y = 1$

2. $x = 2(y + 1)^2 - 6$
$x + 3y = 5$

3. $y^2 - 3x^2 = 6$
$y = 2x - 1$

4. $x + 2y^2 = 4$
$y = -x + 1$

Graph each system of equations. Then find the solutions of each system.

5. $y = x^2$
$y = -x + 2$

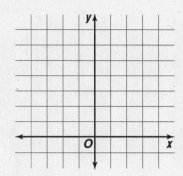

6. $4y^2 - 9x^2 = 36$
$4x^2 - 9y^2 = 36$

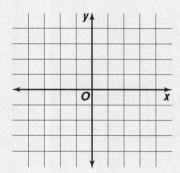

Solve each system of inequalities by graphing.

7. $x^2 + y^2 < 36$
$x^2 + y^2 \geq 16$

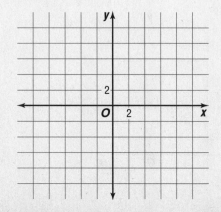

8. $\dfrac{(x + 2)^2}{4} + \dfrac{(y - 3)^2}{16} \leq 1$
$(x + 1)^2 + (y - 2)^2 \leq 4$

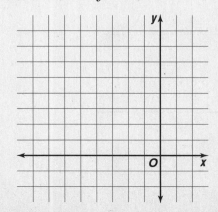

Practice

Solving Quadratic Systems

Solve each system of equations.

1. $(x - 2)^2 + y^2 = 5$
$x - y = 1$
$(0, -1), (3, 2)$

2. $x = 2(y + 1)^2 - 6$
$x + 3y = 5$
$(2, 1), \left(\frac{37}{2}, -\frac{9}{2}\right)$

3. $y^2 - 3x^2 = 6$
$y = 2x - 1$
$(-1, -3), (5, 9)$

4. $x + 2y^2 = 4$
$y = -x + 1$
$(2, -1), \left(-\frac{1}{2}, \frac{3}{2}\right)$

Graph each system of equations. Then find the solutions of each system.

5. $y = x^2$
$y = -x + 2$ $(-2, 4), (1, 1)$

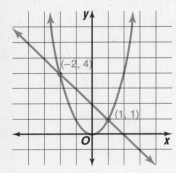

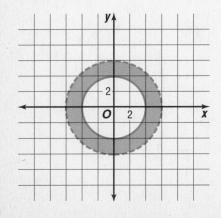

6. $4y^2 - 9x^2 = 36$
$4x^2 - 9y^2 = 36$ **No solutions**

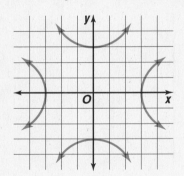

Solve each system of inequalities by graphing.

7. $x^2 + y^2 < 36$
$x^2 + y^2 \geq 16$

8. $\frac{(x + 2)^2}{4} + \frac{(y - 3)^2}{16} \leq 1$
$(x + 1)^2 + (y - 2)^2 \leq 4$

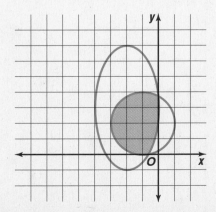

NAME_____ DATE _____

Practice

Polynomial Functions

Find f(3) for each function.

1. $f(x) = x^2 - 6x + 2$

2. $f(x) = x^4 - x^2$

3. $f(x) = -5x^3 + 6x^2 - x - 4$

4. $f(x) = \dfrac{x^2}{6} + 4x - 10$

Find h(−2) for each function.

5. $h(x) = x^3 - x^5$

6. $h(x) = -7x^2 + 5x + 9$

7. $h(x) = x^2 - \dfrac{5x}{4} + 6$

8. $h(x) = 3x^3 - 7x^2 + 2x - 5$

Find g(x + h) for each function.

9. $g(x) = 6x - 7$

10. $g(x) = 3x^2 - 4x + 6$

11. $g(x) = -2x^2 + 5x - 4$

12. $g(x) = x^3 - 2x$

Find 5[f(x + 2)] for each function.

13. $f(x) = 3x^2 - 4$

14. $f(x) = x + 8$

15. $f(x) = 3x - 4$

16. $f(x) = 2x^2 - 5x + 1$

NAME_____ DATE _____

Practice

Polynomial Functions

Find f(3) for each function.

1. $f(x) = x^2 - 6x + 2$ **−7**

2. $f(x) = x^4 - x^2$ **72**

3. $f(x) = -5x^3 + 6x^2 - x - 4$ **−88**

4. $f(x) = \dfrac{x^2}{6} + 4x - 10$ **$\dfrac{7}{2}$**

Find h(−2) for each function.

5. $h(x) = x^3 - x^5$ **24**

6. $h(x) = -7x^2 + 5x + 9$ **−29**

7. $h(x) = x^2 - \dfrac{5x}{4} + 6$ **$\dfrac{25}{2}$**

8. $h(x) = 3x^3 - 7x^2 + 2x - 5$ **−61**

Find g(x + h) for each function.

9. $g(x) = 6x - 7$ **6x + 6h − 7**

10. $g(x) = 3x^2 - 4x + 6$
3x² + 6xh + 3h² − 4x − 4h + 6

11. $g(x) = -2x^2 + 5x - 4$
−2x² − 4xh − 2h² + 5x + 5h − 4

12. $g(x) = x^3 - 2x$
x³ + 3x²h + 3xh² + h³ − 2x − 2h

Find 5[f(x + 2)] for each function.

13. $f(x) = 3x^2 - 4$ **15x² + 60x + 40**

14. $f(x) = x + 8$ **5x + 50**

15. $f(x) = 3x - 4$
15x + 10

16. $f(x) = 2x^2 - 5x + 1$
10x² + 15x − 5

Algebra 2

Practice

The Remainder and Factor Theorems

Divide using synthetic division and write your answer in the form dividend = quotient · divisor + remainder. Is the binomial a factor of the polynomial?

1. $(4x^3 - 9x^2 - 10x - 2) \div (x - 3)$

2. $(2x^3 + 5x^2 - 9x + 20) \div (x + 4)$

3. $(x^4 - 6x^3 - 2x - 10) \div (x + 1)$

4. $(3x^4 - 9x^3 - 32x^2 + 54) \div (x - 5)$

Given a polynomial and one of its factors, find the remaining factors of the polynomial. Some factors may not be binomials.

5. $x^3 + 6x^2 - x - 30; x + 5$

6. $x^3 - 11x^2 + 36x - 36; x - 6$

7. $2x^3 + 3x^2 - 65x + 84; x - 4$

8. $2x^3 + 15x^2 - 14x - 48; x - 2$

9. $16x^5 + 32x^4 - x - 2; x + 2$

10. $x^4 - 3x^3 + 27x - 81; x - 3$

Find values for k so that each remainder is 5.

11. $(2x^2 - 8x + k) \div (x - 7)$

12. $(x^3 + 4x^2 + kx + 8) \div (x + 2)$

13. $(x^4 + kx^3 - 7x^2 + 8x + 25) \div (x - 2)$

14. $(x^2 + 2x + 6) \div (x + k)$

The Remainder and Factor Theorems

Divide using synthetic division and write your answer in the form dividend = quotient · divisor + remainder. Is the binomial a factor of the polynomial?

1. $(4x^3 - 9x^2 - 10x - 2) \div (x - 3)$
$4x^3 - 9x^2 - 10x - 2 =$
$(4x^2 + 3x - 1)(x - 3) - 5$; no

2. $(2x^3 + 5x^2 - 9x + 20) \div (x + 4)$
$2x^3 + 5x^2 - 9x + 20 =$
$(2x^2 - 3x + 3)(x + 4) + 8$; no

3. $(x^4 - 6x^3 - 2x - 10) \div (x + 1)$
$x^4 - 6x^3 - 2x - 10 =$
$(x^3 - 7x^2 + 7x - 9)(x + 1) - 1$; no

4. $(3x^4 - 9x^3 - 32x^2 + 54) \div (x - 5)$
$3x^4 - 9x^3 - 32x^2 + 54 =$
$(3x^3 + 6x^2 - 2x - 10)(x - 5) + 4$;
no

Given a polynomial and one of its factors, find the remaining factors of the polynomial. Some factors may not be binomials.

5. $x^3 + 6x^2 - x - 30; x + 5$
$x + 3, x - 2$

6. $x^3 - 11x^2 + 36x - 36; x - 6$
$x - 3, x - 2$

7. $2x^3 + 3x^2 - 65x + 84; x - 4$
$2x - 3, x + 7$

8. $2x^3 + 15x^2 - 14x - 48; x - 2$
$2x + 3, x + 8$

9. $16x^5 + 32x^4 - x - 2; x + 2$
$4x^2 + 1, 2x + 1, 2x - 1$

10. $x^4 - 3x^3 + 27x - 81; x - 3$
$x + 3, x^2 - 3x + 9$

Find values for k so that each remainder is 5.

11. $(2x^2 - 8x + k) \div (x - 7)$
-37

12. $(x^3 + 4x^2 + kx + 8) \div (x + 2)$
5.5

13. $(x^4 + kx^3 - 7x^2 + 8x + 25) \div (x - 2)$
-3

14. $(x^2 + 2x + 6) \div (x + k)$
1

NAME_____ DATE _____

Practice

Graphing Polynomial Functions and Approximating Zeros

Approximate the real zeros of each function to the nearest tenth.

1. $f(x) = x^3 - 3x^2 + 4$

2. $f(x) = x^3 - 7x + 6$

3. $f(x) = x^3 + 6x^2 + 11x + 3$

4. $f(x) = x^3 - 6x^2 + 8x - 2$

5. $f(x) = x^3 + 3x^2 - 4x - 6$

6. $f(x) = x^3 + x^2 - x + 15$

7. $f(x) = x^4 - 2x^3 + 2x^2 - 5x + 4$

8. $f(x) = x^6 + 2x^4 - x^2 - 4$

Graph each function.

9. $f(x) = (x - 2)^3$

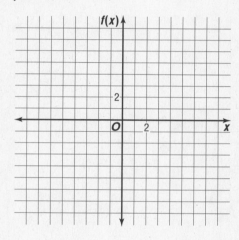

10. $f(x) = (x + 1)^4 - 3$

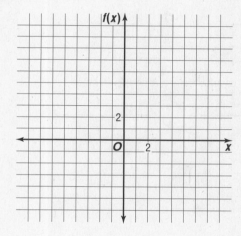

11. $f(x) = x^3 - 3x^2 - x + 3$

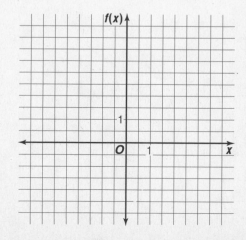

12. $f(x) = x^4 - 9x^2$

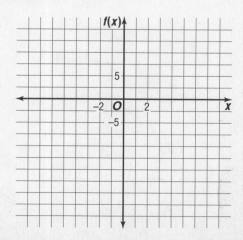

Algebra 2

NAME_____ DATE _____

Practice

Graphing Polynomial Functions and Approximating Zeros

Approximate the real zeros of each function to the nearest tenth.

1. $f(x) = x^3 - 3x^2 + 4$
   −1.0, 2.0

2. $f(x) = x^3 - 7x + 6$
   −3.0, 1.0, 2.0

3. $f(x) = x^3 + 6x^2 + 11x + 3$
   −0.3

4. $f(x) = x^3 - 6x^2 + 8x - 2$
   0.3, 1.5, 4.2

5. $f(x) = x^3 + 3x^2 - 4x - 6$
   −3.6, −1, 1.6

6. $f(x) = x^3 + x^2 - x + 15$
   −3.0

7. $f(x) = x^4 - 2x^3 + 2x^2 - 5x + 4$
   1.0, 1.7

8. $f(x) = x^6 + 2x^4 - x^2 - 4$
   −1.1, 1.1

Graph each function.

9. $f(x) = (x - 2)^3$

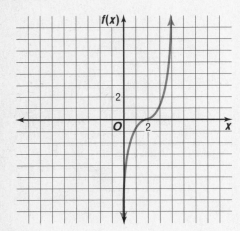

10. $f(x) = (x + 1)^4 - 3$

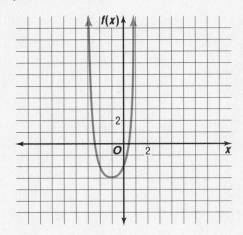

11. $f(x) = x^3 - 3x^2 - x + 3$

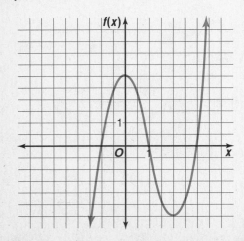

12. $f(x) = x^4 - 9x^2$

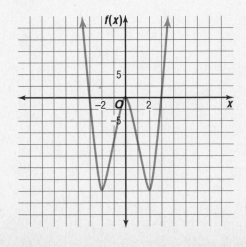

NAME_____ DATE _____

Practice

Roots and Zeros

For each function, state the number of positive real zeros, negative real zeros, and imaginary zeros.

1. $f(x) = 2x^4 - 2x^3 + 2x^2 - x - 1$

2. $f(x) = 4x^3 - 2x^2 + x + 3$

3. $f(x) = 3x^4 + x^3 - 3x^2 + 7x + 5$

4. $f(x) = 7x^4 + 3x^3 - 2x^2 - x + 1$

5. $f(x) = 5x^6 + 7x^4 + 8x^2 + 3$

6. $f(x) = x^5 - x^4 + x^3 + x - 7$

Given a function and one of its zeros, find all of the zeros of the function.

7. $f(x) = x^3 - 7x^2 + 17x - 15; \; 2 + i$

8. $f(x) = x^3 + 6x + 20; \; 1 - 3i$

9. $g(x) = x^4 - 6x^3 + 6x^2 + 24x - 40; \; 3 + i$

10. $g(x) = x^3 - 3x^2 + 9x - 7; \; 1$

Write the polynomial function of least degree with integral coefficients that has the given zeros.

11. $6, 2i$

12. $4, -1, -3i$

13. $i, -5i$

14. $1 + 2i, 1 - i$

Solve.

15. On the first day of school, Kyle lost his class schedule. He remembers that math is not the first class. History is before English and band. Band is after history and English. Neither math nor English is the fourth class, and math is before English. Reconstruct Kyle's class schedule.

NAME _____ DATE _____

Practice

Roots and Zeros

For each function, state the number of positive real zeros, negative real zeros, and imaginary zeros.

1. $f(x) = 2x^4 - 2x^3 + 2x^2 - x - 1$
   3 or 1; 1; 0 or 2

2. $f(x) = 4x^3 - 2x^2 + x + 3$
   2 or 0; 1; 0 or 2

3. $f(x) = 3x^4 + x^3 - 3x^2 + 7x + 5$
   2 or 0; 2 or 0; 0, 2, or 4

4. $f(x) = 7x^4 + 3x^3 - 2x^2 - x + 1$
   2 or 0; 2 or 0; 0, 2, or 4

5. $f(x) = 5x^6 + 7x^4 + 8x^2 + 3$
   0; 0; 6

6. $f(x) = x^5 - x^4 + x^3 + x - 7$
   3 or 1; 0; 2 or 4

Given a function and one of its zeros, find all of the zeros of the function.

7. $f(x) = x^3 - 7x^2 + 17x - 15; 2 + i$
   $2 - i, 3$

8. $f(x) = x^3 + 6x + 20; 1 - 3i$
   $1 + 3i, -2$

9. $g(x) = x^4 - 6x^3 + 6x^2 + 24x - 40; 3 + i$
   $3 - i, 2, -2$

10. $g(x) = x^3 - 3x^2 + 9x - 7; 1$
    $1 + i\sqrt{6}, 1 - i\sqrt{6}$

Write the polynomial function of least degree with integral coefficients that has the given zeros.

11. $6, 2i$
    $f(x) = x^3 - 6x^2 + 4x - 24$

12. $4, -1, -3i$
    $f(x) = x^4 - 3x^3 + 5x^2 - 27x - 36$

13. $i, -5i$
    $f(x) = x^4 + 26x^2 + 25$

14. $1 + 2i, 1 - i$
    $f(x) = x^4 - 4x^3 + 11x^2 - 14x + 10$

Solve.

15. On the first day of school, Kyle lost his class schedule. He remembers that math is not the first class. History is before English and band. Band is after history and English. Neither math nor English is the fourth class, and math is before English. Reconstruct Kyle's class schedule.

    1st: History
    2nd: Math
    3rd: English
    4th: Band

 Algebra 2

Practice

Rational Zero Theorem

List all possible rational zeros for each function.

1. $f(x) = x^3 - 5x^2 + 2x + 12$

2. $f(x) = x^4 - 8x^3 + 7x - 14$

3. $f(x) = 5x^4 - 2x - 4$

4. $f(x) = 3x^5 - 7x^2 + x + 6$

Find all of the rational zeros for each function.

5. $f(x) = x^3 + 3x^2 - 6x - 8$

6. $f(x) = x^3 + 7x^2 + 7x - 15$

7. $f(x) = x^3 - 9x^2 + 27x - 27$

8. $f(x) = x^3 - x^2 - 8x + 12$

9. $f(x) = x^4 - 3x^3 - 11x^2 + 3x + 10$

10. $f(x) = x^4 - 4x^3 - 7x^2 + 34x - 24$

11. $f(x) = x^4 - 2x^3 - 4x^2 + 11x - 6$

12. $f(x) = x^3 + 4x^2 - 2x + 15$

Find all of the zeros of each function.

13. $f(x) = 3x^3 - 4x^2 - 17x + 6$

14. $f(x) = 4x^3 - 12x^2 - x + 3$

15. $f(x) = 18x^3 + 9x^2 - 2x - 1$

16. $f(x) = 2x^3 + 3x^2 + 5x + 2$

17. $f(x) = 2x^4 + 7x^3 - 2x^2 - 19x - 12$

18. $f(x) = x^4 - 4x^3 + x^2 + 16x - 20$

Algebra 2

Rational Zero Theorem

List all possible rational zeros for each function.

1. $f(x) = x^3 - 5x^2 + 2x + 12$
$\pm 1, \pm 2, \pm 3, \pm 4, \pm 6, \pm 12$

2. $f(x) = x^4 - 8x^3 + 7x - 14$
$\pm 1, \pm 2, \pm 7, \pm 14$

3. $f(x) = 5x^4 - 2x - 4$
$\pm 1, \pm\dfrac{1}{5}; \pm 2, \pm\dfrac{2}{5}, \pm 4, \pm\dfrac{4}{5}$

4. $f(x) = 3x^5 - 7x^2 + x + 6$
$\pm 1, \pm\dfrac{1}{3}, \pm 2, \pm\dfrac{2}{3}, \pm 3, \pm 6$

Find all of the rational zeros for each function.

5. $f(x) = x^3 + 3x^2 - 6x - 8$
$2, -1, -4$

6. $f(x) = x^3 + 7x^2 + 7x - 15$
$1, -3, -5$

7. $f(x) = x^3 - 9x^2 + 27x - 27$
3

8. $f(x) = x^3 - x^2 - 8x + 12$
$2, -3$

9. $f(x) = x^4 - 3x^3 - 11x^2 + 3x + 10$
$1, 5, -1, -2$

10. $f(x) = x^4 - 4x^3 - 7x^2 + 34x - 24$
$1, 2, 4, -3$

11. $f(x) = x^4 - 2x^3 - 4x^2 + 11x - 6$
$1, 2$

12. $f(x) = x^3 + 4x^2 - 2x + 15$
-5

Find all of the zeros of each function.

13. $f(x) = 3x^3 - 4x^2 - 17x + 6$
$-2, 3, \dfrac{1}{3}$

14. $f(x) = 4x^3 - 12x^2 - x + 3$
$3, \dfrac{1}{2}, -\dfrac{1}{2}$

15. $f(x) = 18x^3 + 9x^2 - 2x - 1$
$-\dfrac{1}{2}, \dfrac{1}{3}, -\dfrac{1}{3}$

16. $f(x) = 2x^3 + 3x^2 + 5x + 2$
$-\dfrac{1}{2}, \dfrac{-1 \pm i\sqrt{7}}{2}$

17. $f(x) = 2x^4 + 7x^3 - 2x^2 - 19x - 12$
$-1, -3, \dfrac{1 \pm \sqrt{33}}{4}$

18. $f(x) = x^4 - 4x^3 + x^2 + 16x - 20$
$2, -2, 2 \pm i$

Practice

Using Quadratic Techniques to Solve Polynomial Equations

Solve each equation.

1. $x^4 - 50x^2 + 49 = 0$

2. $t^4 - 21t^2 + 80 = 0$

3. $m^4 - 625 = 0$

4. $n^4 - 49n^2 = 0$

5. $w - 12\sqrt{w} + 27 = 0$

6. $n - 10\sqrt{n} + 25 = 0$

7. $y^6 - 8y^3 = 0$

8. $n^6 - 1 = 0$

9. $x^{\frac{1}{2}} - 5x^{\frac{1}{4}} + 6 = 0$

10. $r^{\frac{2}{3}} - r^{\frac{1}{3}} - 20 = 0$

11. $x^{\frac{4}{3}} - 29x^{\frac{2}{3}} + 100 = 0$

12. $y^3 - 28y^{\frac{3}{2}} + 27 = 0$

13. $y^{-1} - 8y^{-\frac{1}{2}} + 12 = 0$

14. $y^{-\frac{2}{3}} - 7y^{-\frac{1}{3}} + 12 = 0$

Practice

Using Quadratic Techniques to Solve Polynomial Equations

Solve each equation.

1. $x^4 - 50x^2 + 49 = 0$
$\pm 7, \pm 1$

2. $t^4 - 21t^2 + 80 = 0$
$\pm\sqrt{5}, \pm 4$

3. $m^4 - 625 = 0$
$\pm 5, \pm 5i$

4. $n^4 - 49n^2 = 0$
$0, \pm 7$

5. $w - 12\sqrt{w} + 27 = 0$
$9, 81$

6. $n - 10\sqrt{n} + 25 = 0$
25

7. $y^6 - 8y^3 = 0$
$0, 2, -1 \pm i\sqrt{3}$

8. $n^6 - 1 = 0$
$\pm 1, \dfrac{-1 \pm i\sqrt{3}}{2}, \dfrac{1 \pm i\sqrt{3}}{2}$

9. $x^{\frac{1}{2}} - 5x^{\frac{1}{4}} + 6 = 0$
$16, 81$

10. $r^{\frac{2}{3}} - r^{\frac{1}{3}} - 20 = 0$
$125, -64$

11. $x^{\frac{4}{3}} - 29x^{\frac{2}{3}} + 100 = 0$
$8, 125$

12. $y^3 - 28y^{\frac{3}{2}} + 27 = 0$
$1, 9$

13. $y^{-1} - 8y^{-\frac{1}{2}} + 12 = 0$
$\dfrac{1}{36}, \dfrac{1}{4}$

14. $y^{-\frac{2}{3}} - 7y^{-\frac{1}{3}} + 12 = 0$
$\dfrac{1}{27}, \dfrac{1}{64}$

Practice

Composition of Functions

Find $[f \circ g](2)$ and $[g \circ f](2)$.

1. $f(x) = 2x - 1$
   $g(x) = -3x$

2. $f(x) = x^2 - 5$
   $g(x) = 3x^2 + 1$

Find $f[g(x)]$ and $g[f(x)]$.

3. $f(x) = x - 8$
   $g(x) = x + 8$

4. $f(x) = x^2 - x + 3$
   $g(x) = |x|$

Find $f[g(-3)]$ and $g[f(-3)]$.

5. $f(x) = 9$
   $g(x) = \dfrac{1}{x}$

6. $f(x) = \sqrt{x + 5}$
   $g(x) = 2x + 8$

If $f(x) = x^2$, $g(x) = 5x$, and $h(x) = x + 4$, find each value.

7. $f[g(1)]$

8. $g[h(-2)]$

9. $h[f(4)]$

10. $f[h(-9)]$

Express $g \circ f$ and $f \circ g$, if they exist, as sets of ordered pairs.

11. $f = \{(3, 8), (2, 5), (4, -5), (9, 3)\}$
    $g = \{(9, 2), (-5, 3), (5, 9), (8, 10), (1, 9)\}$

12. $f = \{(1, 4), (10, 5), (6, -3)\}$
    $g = \{(5, 1), (4, 6), (-3, 10)\}$

Composition of Functions

Find [f ∘ g](2) and [g ∘ f](2).

1. $f(x) = 2x - 1$
   $g(x) = -3x$ **−13; −9**

2. $f(x) = x^2 - 5$
   $g(x) = 3x^2 + 1$ **164; 4**

Find f[g(x)] and g[f(x)].

3. $f(x) = x - 8$
   $g(x) = x + 8$ **x; x**

4. $f(x) = x^2 - x + 3$
   $g(x) = |x|$ **x² − |x| + 3; |x² − x + 3|**

Find f[g(−3)] and g[f(−3)].

5. $f(x) = 9$
   $g(x) = \dfrac{1}{x}$ **9; $\dfrac{1}{9}$**

6. $f(x) = \sqrt{x + 5}$
   $g(x) = 2x + 8$ **$\sqrt{7}$; $2\sqrt{2} + 8$**

If f(x) = x², g(x) = 5x, and h(x) = x + 4, find each value.

7. $f[g(1)]$ **25**

8. $g[h(-2)]$ **10**

9. $h[f(4)]$ **20**

10. $f[h(-9)]$ **25**

Express g ∘ f and f ∘ g, if they exist, as sets of ordered pairs.

11. $f = \{(3, 8), (2, 5), (4, -5), (9, 3)\}$
    $g = \{(9, 2), (-5, 3), (5, 9), (8, 10), (1, 9)\}$
    g ∘ f doesn't exist
    f ∘ g doesn't exist

12. $f = \{(1, 4), (10, 5), (6, -3)\}$
    $g = \{(5, 1), (4, 6), (-3, 10)\}$
    g ∘ f = {(1, 6), (10, 1), (6, 10)}
    f ∘ g = {(5, 4), (4, −3), (−3, 5)}

Practice

Inverse Functions and Relations

Find the inverse of each relation and determine whether the inverse is a function.

1. $f(x) = 2x + 5$

2. $y = 7$

3. $y = 3 - x$

4. $f(x) = x^2 - 1$

Determine whether each pair of functions are inverse functions.

5. $f(x) = x + 5$
   $g(x) = x - 5$

6. $f(x) = \frac{1}{2}x + 2$
   $g(x) = 2x - 4$

7. $f(x) = 4 - x$
   $g(x) = 4 + x$

8. $f(x) = 3x - 9$
   $g(x) = -3x + 9$

Find the inverse of each function. Then graph each function and its inverse.

9. $f(x) = x^2 - 3$

10. $f(x) = -4x$

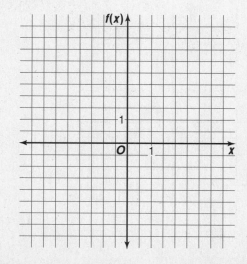

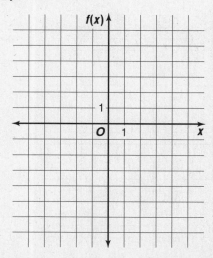

Inverse Functions and Relations

Find the inverse of each relation and determine whether the inverse is a function.

1. $f(x) = 2x + 5$ $f^{-1}(x) = \frac{1}{2}x - \frac{5}{2}$; **yes**

2. $y = 7$ $x = 7$; **no**

3. $y = 3 - x$ $y = 3 - x$; **yes**

4. $f(x) = x^2 - 1$ $f^{-1}(x) = \pm\sqrt{x + 1}$; **no**

Determine whether each pair of functions are inverse functions.

5. $f(x) = x + 5$
   $g(x) = x - 5$ **yes**

6. $f(x) = \frac{1}{2}x + 2$
   $g(x) = 2x - 4$ **yes**

7. $f(x) = 4 - x$
   $g(x) = 4 + x$ **no**

8. $f(x) = 3x - 9$
   $g(x) = -3x + 9$ **no**

Find the inverse of each function. Then graph each function and its inverse.

9. $f(x) = x^2 - 3$ $f^{-1}(x) = \pm\sqrt{x + 3}$

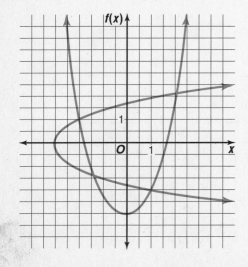

10. $f(x) = -4x$ $f^{-1}(x) = -\frac{1}{4}x$

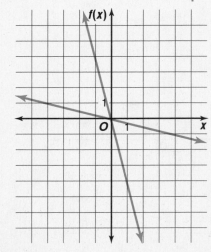

Algebra 2

NAME_____ DATE_____

Practice

Graphing Rational Functions

Graph each rational function.

1. $y = \dfrac{-4}{x - 2}$

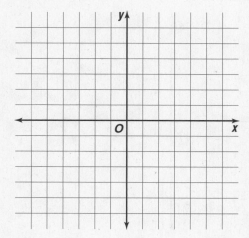

2. $y = \dfrac{3}{(x + 1)(x - 1)}$

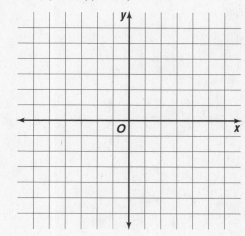

3. $y = \dfrac{x}{x + 3}$

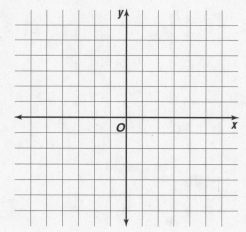

4. $y = \dfrac{-5}{x + 1}$

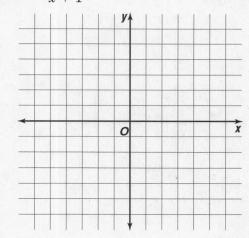

5. $y = \dfrac{3x}{(x + 3)^2}$

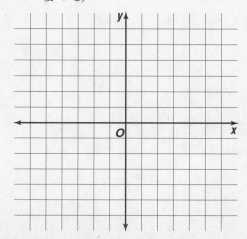

6. $y = \dfrac{x - 3}{x - 2}$

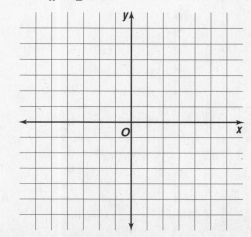

Practice

Graphing Rational Functions

Graph each rational function.

1. $y = \dfrac{-4}{x-2}$

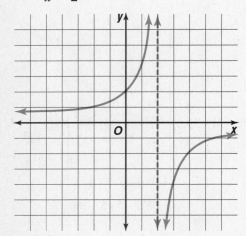

2. $y = \dfrac{3}{(x+1)(x-1)}$

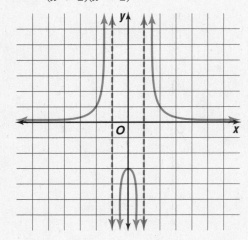

3. $y = \dfrac{x}{x+3}$

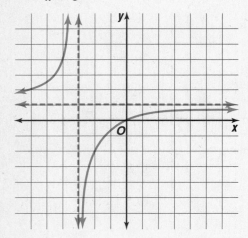

4. $y = \dfrac{-5}{x+1}$

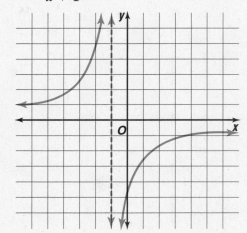

5. $y = \dfrac{3x}{(x+3)^2}$

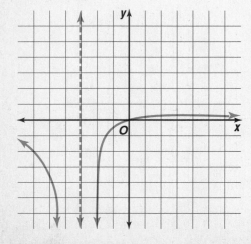

6. $y = \dfrac{x-3}{x-2}$

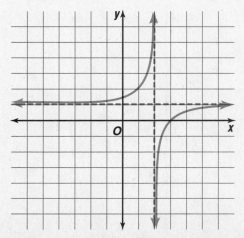

Algebra 2

Practice

Direct, Inverse, and Joint Variation

Write an equation for each statement. Then solve the equation.

1. Find y when $x = 6$, if y varies directly as x and $y = 8$ when $x = 2$.

2. Find y when $x = 1.5$, if y varies directly as x and $y = -16$ when $x = 6$.

3. Find y when $x = 4$, if y varies directly as x and $y = 7$ when $x = 1.5$.

4. Find y when $x = 5$, if y varies directly as x and $y = 5$ when $x = 3.5$.

5. Find x when $y = 3$, if y varies inversely as x and $x = 4$, when $y = 16$.

6. Find x when $y = 5$, if y varies inversely as x and $x = 6$ when $y = -18$.

7. Find y when $x = 2\frac{1}{2}$, if y varies inversely as x and $x = 5$ when $y = 3$.

8. Find y when $x = 10$, if y varies inversely as x and $x = 7.5$ when $y = 6$.

9. Find y when $x = 4$ and $z = 15$, if y varies jointly as x and z and $y = 5$ when $z = 8$ and $x = 10$.

10. Find y when $x = 12$ and $z = 2$, if y varies jointly as x and z and $y = 24$ when $z = 2$ and $x = 1$.

11. Find y when $x = 6$ and $z = 8$, if y varies jointly as x and z and $y = 60$ when $x = 3$ and $z = 4$.

12. Find y when $x = 4$ and $z = -1$, if y varies jointly as x and z and $y = 12$ when $x = -2$ and $z = 3$.

Practice

Direct, Inverse, and Joint Variation

Write an equation for each statement. Then solve the equation.

1. Find y when $x = 6$, if y varies directly as x and $y = 8$ when $x = 2$.

$$\frac{y}{6} = \frac{8}{2};\ 24$$

2. Find y when $x = 1.5$, if y varies directly as x and $y = -16$ when $x = 6$.

$$\frac{y}{1.5} = \frac{-16}{6};\ -4$$

3. Find y when $x = 4$, if y varies directly as x and $y = 7$ when $x = 1.5$.

$$\frac{y}{4} = \frac{7}{1.5};\ \frac{56}{3}$$

4. Find y when $x = 5$, if y varies directly as x and $y = 5$ when $x = 3.5$.

$$\frac{y}{5} = \frac{5}{3.5};\ \frac{50}{7}$$

5. Find x when $y = 3$, if y varies inversely as x and $x = 4$, when $y = 16$.

$$\frac{x}{16} = \frac{4}{3};\ \frac{64}{3}$$

6. Find x when $y = 5$, if y varies inversely as x and $x = 6$ when $y = -18$.

$$\frac{x}{-18} = \frac{6}{5};\ -21.6$$

7. Find y when $x = 2\frac{1}{2}$, if y varies inversely as x and $x = 5$ when $y = 3$.

$$\frac{2.5}{3} = \frac{5}{y};\ 6$$

8. Find y when $x = 10$, if y varies inversely as x and $x = 7.5$ when $y = 6$.

$$\frac{10}{6} = \frac{7.5}{y};\ 4.5$$

9. Find y when $x = 4$ and $z = 15$, if y varies jointly as x and z and $y = 5$ when $z = 8$ and $x = 10$.

$$y = \frac{1}{16} \cdot 4 \cdot 15;\ \frac{15}{4}$$

10. Find y when $x = 12$ and $z = 2$, if y varies jointly as x and z and $y = 24$ when $z = 2$ and $x = 1$.

$$y = 12 \cdot 12 \cdot 2;\ 288$$

11. Find y when $x = 6$ and $z = 8$, if y varies jointly as x and z and $y = 60$ when $x = 3$ and $z = 4$.

$$y = 5 \cdot 6 \cdot 8;\ 240$$

12. Find y when $x = 4$ and $z = -1$, if y varies jointly as x and z and $y = 12$ when $x = -2$ and $z = 3$.

$$y = -2 \cdot 4 \cdot -1;\ 8$$

NAME_____ DATE _____

Practice

Student Edition
Pages 562–568

Multiplying and Dividing Rational Expressions

Simplify each expression.

1. $\dfrac{a+y}{6} \cdot \dfrac{4}{y+a}$

2. $\dfrac{a-y}{w+n} \cdot \dfrac{w^2-n^2}{y-a}$

3. $\dfrac{x^2-5x-24}{6x+2x^2} \cdot \dfrac{5x^2}{8-x}$

4. $\dfrac{n^5}{n-6} \cdot \dfrac{n^2-6n}{n^8}$

5. $\dfrac{a^5y^3}{wy^7} \div \dfrac{a^3w^2}{w^5y^2}$

6. $\left(\dfrac{2xy}{w^2}\right)^3 \div \dfrac{24x^2}{w^5}$

7. $\dfrac{x+y}{6} \div \dfrac{x^2-y^2}{3}$

8. $\dfrac{3x+6}{x^2-9} \div \dfrac{6x^2+12x}{4x+12}$

9. $\dfrac{\dfrac{x^2-9}{4}}{\dfrac{3-x}{8}}$

10. $\dfrac{\dfrac{1}{x}+2}{\dfrac{4}{x}-1}$

11. $\dfrac{\dfrac{y^4-81}{xy+4y+3x+12}}{y^2+9}$

12. $\dfrac{\dfrac{x^3+2^3}{x^2-2x}}{\dfrac{(x+2)^3}{x^2+4x+4}}$

NAME _____ DATE _____

Practice

Multiplying and Dividing Rational Expressions

Simplify each expression.

1. $\dfrac{a+y}{6} \cdot \dfrac{4}{y+a}$ $\dfrac{2}{3}$

2. $\dfrac{a-y}{w+n} \cdot \dfrac{w^2-n^2}{y-a}$ $n-w$

3. $\dfrac{x^2-5x-24}{6x+2x^2} \cdot \dfrac{5x^2}{8-x}$ $-\dfrac{5x}{2}$

4. $\dfrac{n^5}{n-6} \cdot \dfrac{n^2-6n}{n^8}$ $\dfrac{1}{n^2}$

5. $\dfrac{a^5y^3}{wy^7} \div \dfrac{a^3w^2}{w^5y^2}$ $\dfrac{a^2w^2}{y^2}$

6. $\left(\dfrac{2xy}{w^2}\right)^3 \div \dfrac{24x^2}{w^5}$ $\dfrac{xy^3}{3w}$

7. $\dfrac{x+y}{6} \div \dfrac{x^2-y^2}{3}$ $\dfrac{1}{2(x-y)}$

8. $\dfrac{3x+6}{x^2-9} \div \dfrac{6x^2+12x}{4x+12}$ $\dfrac{2}{x(x-3)}$

9. $\dfrac{\dfrac{x^2-9}{4}}{\dfrac{3-x}{8}}$ $-2(x+3)$

10. $\dfrac{\dfrac{1}{x}+2}{\dfrac{4}{x}-1}$ $\dfrac{1+2x}{4-x}$

11. $\dfrac{\dfrac{y^4-81}{xy+4y+3x+12}}{\dfrac{y^2+9}{}}$ $\dfrac{y-3}{x+4}$

12. $\dfrac{\dfrac{x^3+2^3}{x^2-2x}}{\dfrac{(x+2)^3}{x^2+4x+4}}$ $\dfrac{x^2-2x+4}{x(x-2)}$

Algebra 2

Practice

Adding and Subtracting Rational Expressions

Simplify each expression.

1. $\dfrac{5}{6ab} - \dfrac{7}{8a}$

2. $2x - 5 - \dfrac{x-8}{x+4}$

3. $\dfrac{4}{a-3} + \dfrac{9}{a-5}$

4. $\dfrac{16}{x^2-16} + \dfrac{2}{x+4}$

5. $\dfrac{5}{2x-12} - \dfrac{20}{x^2-4x-12}$

6. $\dfrac{2-5m}{m-9} + \dfrac{4m-5}{9-m}$

7. $\dfrac{2p-3}{p^2-5p+6} - \dfrac{5}{p^2-9}$

8. $\dfrac{1}{5n} - \dfrac{3}{4} + \dfrac{7}{10n}$

9. $\dfrac{\dfrac{r+6}{r} - \dfrac{1}{r+2}}{\dfrac{r^2+4r+3}{r^2+r}}$

10. $\dfrac{n+5-\dfrac{12}{n+1}}{\dfrac{n+9}{n+1}-\dfrac{5}{n}}$

11. $\dfrac{\dfrac{2}{x-y} + \dfrac{1}{x+y}}{\dfrac{1}{x-y}}$

12. $\dfrac{x-\dfrac{5x}{x+2}}{\dfrac{x-3}{x}}$

NAME_____ DATE _____

Practice

Adding and Subtracting Rational Expressions

Simplify each expression.

1. $\dfrac{5}{6ab} - \dfrac{7}{8a}$

$\dfrac{20 - 21b}{24ab}$

2. $2x - 5 - \dfrac{x - 8}{x + 4}$

$\dfrac{2(x + 3)(x - 2)}{x + 4}$

3. $\dfrac{4}{a - 3} + \dfrac{9}{a - 5}$

$\dfrac{13a - 47}{(a - 3)(a - 5)}$

4. $\dfrac{16}{x^2 - 16} + \dfrac{2}{x + 4}$

$\dfrac{2}{x - 4}$

5. $\dfrac{5}{2x - 12} - \dfrac{20}{x^2 - 4x - 12}$

$\dfrac{5}{2(x + 2)}$

6. $\dfrac{2 - 5m}{m - 9} + \dfrac{4m - 5}{9 - m}$

$\dfrac{7 - 9m}{m - 9}$

7. $\dfrac{2p - 3}{p^2 - 5p + 6} - \dfrac{5}{p^2 - 9}$

$\dfrac{2p^2 - 2p + 1}{(p - 2)(p + 3)(p - 3)}$

8. $\dfrac{1}{5n} - \dfrac{3}{4} + \dfrac{7}{10n}$

$\dfrac{3(6 - 5n)}{20n}$

9. $\dfrac{\frac{r + 6}{r} - \frac{1}{r + 2}}{\frac{r^2 + 4r + 3}{r^2 + r}}$

$\dfrac{r + 4}{r + 2}$

10. $\dfrac{n + 5 - \frac{12}{n + 1}}{\frac{n + 9}{n + 1} - \frac{5}{n}}$

$\dfrac{n(n + 7)}{n + 5}$

11. $\dfrac{\frac{2}{x - y} + \frac{1}{x + y}}{\frac{1}{x - y}}$

$\dfrac{3x + y}{x + y}$

12. $\dfrac{x - \frac{5x}{x + 2}}{\frac{x - 3}{x}}$

$\dfrac{x^2}{x + 2}$

9-5

Practice

Solving Rational Equations

Solve each equation. Check your solutions.

1. $\dfrac{12}{x} + \dfrac{3}{4} = \dfrac{3}{2}$

2. $\dfrac{x^2}{8} - 4 = \dfrac{x}{2}$

3. $\dfrac{x + 10}{x^2 - 2} = \dfrac{4}{x}$

4. $\dfrac{x}{x + 2} + x = \dfrac{5x + 8}{x + 2}$

5. $\dfrac{5}{x - 5} = \dfrac{x}{x - 5} - 1$

6. $\dfrac{1}{3x - 2} + \dfrac{5}{x} = 0$

7. $\dfrac{6}{x - 1} = \dfrac{4}{x - 2} + \dfrac{2}{x + 1}$

8. $\dfrac{x + 1}{x - 3} = 4 - \dfrac{12}{x^2 - 2x - 3}$

9. $\dfrac{1}{x - 1} = \dfrac{2}{x + 1} - \dfrac{1}{x + 3}$

10. $\dfrac{1}{x + 2} + \dfrac{1}{x - 2} = \dfrac{3}{x + 1}$

Solve.

11. The view of the rectangular box at the right shows three faces of the box. The areas of two of the faces are 30 cm² and 48 cm². The volume of the box is 240 cm³. What is the area of the third face?

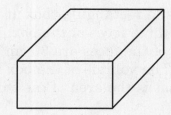

NAME _____ DATE _____

Practice

Solving Rational Equations

Solve each equation. Check your solutions.

1. $\dfrac{12}{x} + \dfrac{3}{4} = \dfrac{3}{2}$ **16**

2. $\dfrac{x^2}{8} - 4 = \dfrac{x}{2}$ **−4, 8**

3. $\dfrac{x + 10}{x^2 - 2} = \dfrac{4}{x}$ **$-\dfrac{2}{3}$, 4**

4. $\dfrac{x}{x + 2} + x = \dfrac{5x + 8}{x + 2}$ **4**

5. $\dfrac{5}{x - 5} = \dfrac{x}{x - 5} - 1$ **all reals except 5**

6. $\dfrac{1}{3x - 2} + \dfrac{5}{x} = 0$ **$\dfrac{5}{8}$**

7. $\dfrac{6}{x - 1} = \dfrac{4}{x - 2} + \dfrac{2}{x + 1}$ **∅**

8. $\dfrac{x + 1}{x - 3} = 4 - \dfrac{12}{x^2 - 2x - 3}$ **$-\dfrac{5}{3}$, 5**

9. $\dfrac{1}{x - 1} = \dfrac{2}{x + 1} - \dfrac{1}{x + 3}$ **∅**

10. $\dfrac{1}{x + 2} + \dfrac{1}{x - 2} = \dfrac{3}{x + 1}$ **$1 \pm \sqrt{13}$**

Solve.

11. The view of the rectangular box at the right shows three faces of the box. The areas of two of the faces are 30 cm² and 48 cm². The volume of the box is 240 cm³. What is the area of the third face? **40 cm²**

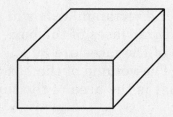

Real Exponents and Exponential Functions

Simplify each expression.

1. $(2^{\sqrt{2}})^{\sqrt{18}}$

2. $13^{\sqrt{6}} \cdot 13^{\sqrt{24}}$

3. $125^{\sqrt{11}} \div 5^{\sqrt{11}}$

4. $(n^{\sqrt{3}})^{\sqrt{75}}$

5. $32^{\sqrt{3}} \cdot 16^{\sqrt{2}}$

6. $(r^{\sqrt{3}} + p^{\sqrt{5}})^2$

7. $(n^{\sqrt{6}} + w^{\sqrt{3}})(n^{\sqrt{6}} - w^{\sqrt{3}})$

8. $(r^{\sqrt{3}} \cdot p^{\sqrt{5}})^2$

Solve each equation.

9. $7^{6x} = 7^{2x - 20}$

10. $3^{6x - 5} = 9^{4x - 3}$

11. $9^{2x - 1} = 27^{x + 4}$

12. $5^{2x + 3} = (\sqrt{5})^{x + 4}$

13. $2^{3x - 1} = \left(\dfrac{1}{8}\right)^{x}$

14. $\left(\dfrac{1}{16}\right)^{x + 1} = \left(\dfrac{1}{8}\right)^{2x - 1}$

Practice

Real Exponents and Exponential Functions

Simplify each expression.

1. $(2^{\sqrt{2}})^{\sqrt{18}}$ **2^6 or 64**

2. $13^{\sqrt{6}} \cdot 13^{\sqrt{24}}$ **$13^{3\sqrt{6}}$**

3. $125^{\sqrt{11}} \div 5^{\sqrt{11}}$ **$5^{2\sqrt{11}}$**

4. $(n^{\sqrt{3}})^{\sqrt{75}}$ **n^{15}**

5. $32^{\sqrt{3}} \cdot 16^{\sqrt{2}}$ **$2^{5\sqrt{3}\,+\,4\sqrt{2}}$**

6. $(r^{\sqrt{3}} + p^{\sqrt{5}})^2$
   $r^{2\sqrt{3}} + 2r^{\sqrt{3}}p^{\sqrt{5}} + p^{2\sqrt{5}}$

7. $(n^{\sqrt{6}} + w^{\sqrt{3}})(n^{\sqrt{6}} - w^{\sqrt{3}})$
   $n^{2\sqrt{6}} - w^{2\sqrt{3}}$

8. $(r^{\sqrt{3}} \cdot p^{\sqrt{5}})^2$ **$r^{2\sqrt{3}} \cdot p^{2\sqrt{5}}$**

Solve each equation.

9. $7^{6x} = 7^{2x-20}$ **-5**

10. $3^{6x-5} = 9^{4x-3}$ **$\dfrac{1}{2}$**

11. $9^{2x-1} = 27^{x+4}$ **14**

12. $5^{2x+3} = (\sqrt{5})^{x+4}$ **$-\dfrac{2}{3}$**

13. $2^{3x-1} = \left(\dfrac{1}{8}\right)^{x}$ **$\dfrac{1}{6}$**

14. $\left(\dfrac{1}{16}\right)^{x+1} = \left(\dfrac{1}{8}\right)^{2x-1}$ **$\dfrac{7}{2}$**

Practice

Logarithms and Logarithmic Functions

Write each equation in logarithmic form.

1. $5^3 = 125$

2. $27^{\frac{4}{3}} = 81$

Write each equation in exponential form.

3. $\log_{10} 0.00001 = -5$

4. $\log_{\frac{3}{2}} \dfrac{\sqrt{6}}{3} = -\dfrac{1}{2}$

Evaluate each expression.

5. $\log_3 81$

6. $\log_{10} 0.0001$

7. $\log_2 \dfrac{1}{16}$

8. $\log_{\frac{1}{3}} 27$

9. $\log_9 1$

10. $\log_8 4$

Solve each equation.

11. $\log_4 x = \dfrac{3}{2}$

12. $\log_y 16 = -4$

13. $\log_a \dfrac{1}{8} = -3$

14. $\log_7 n = -\dfrac{1}{2}$

15. $\log_{\sqrt{5}} y = \dfrac{4}{3}$

16. $\log_x \sqrt[3]{9} = \dfrac{1}{6}$

17. $\log_8(3x + 7) = \log_8(7x + 4)$

18. $\log_7(8x + 20) = \log_7(x + 6)$

19. $\log_3(9x - 1) = \log_3(4x - 16)$

20. $\log_{12}(x - 9) = \log_{12}(3x - 13)$

21. $\log_5(x^2 - 30) = \log_5 6$

22. $\log_4(x^2 + 6) = \log_4 5x$

Algebra 2

Practice

Logarithms and Logarithmic Functions

Write each equation in logarithmic form.

1. $5^3 = 125$ $\log_5 125 = 3$

2. $27^{\frac{4}{3}} = 81$ $\log_{27} 81 = \frac{4}{3}$

Write each equation in exponential form.

3. $\log_{10} 0.00001 = -5$ $10^{-5} = 0.00001$

4. $\log_{\frac{3}{2}} \frac{\sqrt{6}}{3} = -\frac{1}{2}$ $\left(\frac{3}{2}\right)^{-\frac{1}{2}} = \frac{\sqrt{6}}{3}$

Evaluate each expression.

5. $\log_3 81$ **4**

6. $\log_{10} 0.0001$ **−4**

7. $\log_2 \frac{1}{16}$ **−4**

8. $\log_{\frac{1}{3}} 27$ **−3**

9. $\log_9 1$ **0**

10. $\log_8 4$ $\frac{2}{3}$

Solve each equation.

11. $\log_4 x = \frac{3}{2}$ **8**

12. $\log_y 16 = -4$ $\frac{1}{2}$

13. $\log_a \frac{1}{8} = -3$ **2**

14. $\log_7 n = -\frac{1}{2}$ $\frac{\sqrt{7}}{7}$

15. $\log_{\sqrt{5}} y = \frac{4}{3}$ $5^{\frac{2}{3}}$ **or** $\sqrt[3]{25}$

16. $\log_x \sqrt[3]{9} = \frac{1}{6}$ **81**

17. $\log_8(3x + 7) = \log_8(7x + 4)$ $\frac{3}{4}$

18. $\log_7(8x + 20) = \log_7(x + 6)$ **−2**

19. $\log_3(9x - 1) = \log_3(4x - 16)$
no solution

20. $\log_{12}(x - 9) = \log_{12}(3x - 13)$
no solution

21. $\log_5(x^2 - 30) = \log_5 6$ **±6**

22. $\log_4(x^2 + 6) = \log_4 5x$ **2, 3**

     Algebra 2

Practice

Properties of Logarithms

Evaluate each expression.

1. $n^{\log_n 3}$

2. $14^{\log_{14} 6}$

Use $log_{10}\, 5 = 0.6990$ and $log_{10}\, 7 = 0.8451$ to evaluate each expression.

3. $\log_{10} 35$

4. $\log_{10} \dfrac{7}{5}$

5. $\log_{10} 25$

6. $\log_{10} 490$

7. $\log_{10} \left(1\dfrac{3}{7}\right)$

8. $\log_{10} 0.05$

Solve each equation.

9. $\log_6 x + \log_6 9 = \log_6 54$

10. $\log_8 48 - \log_8 w = \log_8 4$

11. $\log_7 n = \dfrac{2}{3} \log_7 8$

12. $\log_3 y = \dfrac{1}{4} \log_3 16 + \dfrac{1}{3} \log_3 64$

13. $\log_9 (3u + 14) - \log_9 5 = \log_9 2u$

14. $\log_7 x + \log_7 x - \log_7 3 = \log_7 12$

15. $4 \log_2 x + \log_2 5 = \log_2 405$

16. $\log_6 (2x - 5) + 1 = \log_6 (7x + 10)$

17. $\log_{16}(9x + 5) - \log_{16}(x^2 - 1) = \dfrac{1}{2}$

18. $\log_8 (n - 3) + \log_8 (n + 4) = 1$

19. $\log_6 (3m + 7) - \log_6 (m + 4) = 2 \log_6 6 - 3 \log_6 3$

20. $\log_2 (2x + 8) - \log_2 (2x^2 + 21x + 61) = -3$

Practice

Properties of Logarithms

Evaluate each expression.

1. $n^{\log_n 3}$ **3**

2. $14^{\log_{14} 6}$ **6**

Use $\log_{10} 5 = 0.6990$ and $\log_{10} 7 = 0.8451$ to evaluate each expression.

3. $\log_{10} 35$ **1.5441**

4. $\log_{10} \dfrac{7}{5}$ **0.1461**

5. $\log_{10} 25$ **1.3980**

6. $\log_{10} 490$ **2.6902**

7. $\log_{10} \left(1\dfrac{3}{7}\right)$ **0.1549**

8. $\log_{10} 0.05$ **−1.3010**

Solve each equation.

9. $\log_6 x + \log_6 9 = \log_6 54$ **6**

10. $\log_8 48 - \log_8 w = \log_8 4$ **12**

11. $\log_7 n = \dfrac{2}{3} \log_7 8$ **4**

12. $\log_3 y = \dfrac{1}{4} \log_3 16 + \dfrac{1}{3} \log_3 64$ **8**

13. $\log_9 (3u + 14) - \log_9 5 = \log_9 2u$ **2**

14. $\log_7 x + \log_7 x - \log_7 3 = \log_7 12$ **6**

15. $4 \log_2 x + \log_2 5 = \log_2 405$ **3**

16. $\log_6(2x - 5) + 1 = \log_6(7x + 10)$ **8**

17. $\log_{16}(9x + 5) - \log_{16}(x^2 - 1) = \dfrac{1}{2}$ **3**

18. $\log_8(n - 3) + \log_8(n + 4) = 1$ **4**

19. $\log_6(3m + 7) - \log_6(m + 4) = 2 \log_6 6 - 3 \log_6 3$ **−1**

20. $\log_2(2x + 8) - \log_2(2x^2 + 21x + 61) = -3$ **$\dfrac{1}{2}$, −3**

Practice

Common Logarithms

Use a scientific calculator to find the logarithm of each number rounded to four decimal places. Then state the characteristic and the mantissa.

1. 95

2. 0.233

3. 4920

4. 30,700

5. 211.3

6. 4.321

7. 8.125

8. 17.654

9. 0.0004764

10. 1.8519

11. 6.437×10^{-9}

12. 0.0125

Use a scientific calculator to find the antilogarithm of each logarithm rounded to four decimal places.

13. 2.63

14. −0.4089

15. 2.9484

16. −2.2168

17. 3.6940

18. 0.6456 − 3

19. 4.8503

20. 0.6164 − 2

21. 5.3

22. 2.384

23. −1.55

24. −3.2479

Algebra 2

Common Logarithms

Use a scientific calculator to find the logarithm of each number rounded to four decimal places. Then state the characteristic and the mantissa.

1. 95 **1.9777;**
   1; 0.9777

2. 0.233 **−0.6326;**
   −1; 0.3674

3. 4920 **3.6920;**
   3; 0.6920

4. 30,700 **4.4871;**
   4; 0.4871

5. 211.3 **2.3249;**
   2; 0.3249

6. 4.321 **0.6356;**
   0; 0.6356

7. 8.125 **0.9098;**
   0; 0.9098

8. 17.654 **1.2468;**
   1; 0.2468

9. 0.0004764 **−3.3220;**
   −4; 0.6780

10. 1.8519 **0.2676;**
    0; 0.2676

11. 6.437×10^{-9} **−8.1913;**
    −9; 0.8086

12. 0.0125 **−1.9031;**
    −2; 0.0969

Use a scientific calculator to find the antilogarithm of each logarithm rounded to four decimal places.

13. 2.63
    426.5795

14. −0.4089
    0.3900

15. 2.9484
    887.9735

16. −2.2168
    0.0061

17. 3.6940
    4943.1069

18. 0.6456 − 3
    0.0044

19. 4.8503
    70,843.4985

20. 0.6164 − 2
    0.0413

21. 5.3
    199,526.2315

22. 2.384
    242.1029

23. −1.55
    0.0282

24. −3.2479
    0.0006

Practice

Natural Logarithms

Use a scientific calculator to find each value, rounded to four decimal places.

1. ln 4.76

2. ln 3.98

3. ln 26.9

4. ln 72.34

5. ln 0.478

6. ln 0.0025

7. ln 894

8. ln 526

9. ln 0.406

10. ln 0.0243

11. antiln 0.8926

12. antiln 0.247

13. antiln 0.9425

14. antiln −0.8679

15. antiln −0.5427

16. antiln 1.876

17. antiln 2.741

18. antiln −1.478

19. antiln 9.42

20. antiln −2.791

NAME _____ DATE _____

Practice

Natural Logarithms

Use a scientific calculator to find each value, rounded to four decimal places.

1. ln 4.76
1.5602

2. ln 3.98
1.3813

3. ln 26.9
3.2921

4. ln 72.34
4.2814

5. ln 0.478
−0.7381

6. ln 0.0025
−5.9915

7. ln 894
6.7957

8. ln 526
6.2653

9. ln 0.406
−0.9014

10. ln 0.0243
−3.7173

11. antiln 0.8926
2.4415

12. antiln 0.247
1.2802

13. antiln 0.9425
2.5664

14. antiln −0.8679
0.4198

15. antiln −0.5427
0.5812

16. antiln 1.876
6.5273

17. antiln 2.741
15.5025

18. antiln −1.478
0.2281

19. antiln 9.42
12,332.5822

20. antiln −2.791
0.0614

Practice

Solving Exponential Equations

Use logarithms to solve each equation.

1. $3.5^x = 47.9$

2. $8.2^y = 64.5$

3. $7.2^{a-4} = 8.21$

4. $2^{b+1} = 7.31$

5. $y = \log_3 78.5$

6. $k = \log_4 91.8$

7. $4^{2x} = 9^{x-1}$

8. $7^{3b} = 12^{b+2}$

9. $17c^{\frac{2}{3}} = 44$

10. $7x^{\frac{9}{8}} = 111$

11. $5^{x^2-3} = 72$

12. $\sqrt[4]{3^{4x+5}} = 7^x$

Solve.

13. Jim wants to paint the walls of a room that is 15 feet wide and 20 feet long. The ceiling is 8 feet high. How many gallons of paint will he need if each gallon covers 350 square feet and he wants to give the room two coats of paint?

NAME_____ DATE _____

Practice

Solving Exponential Equations

Use logarithms to solve each equation.

1. $3.5^x = 47.9$ **3.0885**

2. $8.2^y = 64.5$ **1.9802**

3. $7.2^{a-4} = 8.21$ **5.0665**

4. $2^{b+1} = 7.31$ **1.8699**

5. $y = \log_3 78.5$ **3.9715**

6. $k = \log_4 91.8$ **3.2602**

7. $4^{2x} = 9^{x-1}$ **−3.8188**

8. $7^{3b} = 12^{b+2}$ **1.4823**

9. $17c^{\frac{2}{3}} = 44$ **4.1640**

10. $7x^{\frac{9}{8}} = 111$ **11.6645**

11. $5^{x^2-3} = 72$ **±2.3785**

12. $\sqrt[4]{3^{4x+5}} = 7^x$ **1.6208**

Solve.

13. Jim wants to paint the walls of a room that is 15 feet wide
and 20 feet long. The ceiling is 8 feet high. How many
gallons of paint will he need if each gallon covers 350 square
feet and he wants to give the room two coats of paint?
4 gallons

Practice

Growth and Decay

Solve.

1. Suppose $500 is invested at 6% annual interest compounded twice a year. When will the investment be worth $1000?

2. Suppose $500 is invested at 6% annual interest compounded continuously. When will the investment be worth $1000?

3. An organism of a certain type can grow from 30 to 195 organisms in 5 hours. Find k for the growth formula.

4. For a certain strain of bacteria, k is 0.825 when t is measured in days. How long will it take 20 bacteria to increase to 2000?

5. An investment service promises to triple your money in 12 years. Assuming continuous compounding of interest, what rate of interest is needed?

6. A substance decomposes radioactively. Its half-life is 32 years. Find the constant k in the decay formula.

7. A piece of machinery valued at $250,000 depreciates at 12% per year by the fixed rate method. After how many years will the value have depreciated to $100,000?

8. Dave bought a new car 8 years ago for $8400. To buy a new car comparably equipped now would cost $12,500. Assuming a steady rate of increase, what was the yearly rate of inflation in car prices over the 8-year period?

Practice

Growth and Decay

Solve.

1. Suppose $500 is invested at 6% annual interest compounded twice a year. When will the investment be worth $1000?
11.72 years

2. Suppose $500 is invested at 6% annual interest compounded continuously. When will the investment be worth $1000?
11.55 years

3. An organism of a certain type can grow from 30 to 195 organisms in 5 hours. Find k for the growth formula.
0.3744

4. For a certain strain of bacteria, k is 0.825 when t is measured in days. How long will it take 20 bacteria to increase to 2000?
5.582 days

5. An investment service promises to triple your money in 12 years. Assuming continuous compounding of interest, what rate of interest is needed?
9.155%

6. A substance decomposes radioactively. Its half-life is 32 years. Find the constant k in the decay formula.
−0.02166

7. A piece of machinery valued at $250,000 depreciates at 12% per year by the fixed rate method. After how many years will the value have depreciated to $100,000?
7.168 years

8. Dave bought a new car 8 years ago for $8400. To buy a new car comparably equipped now would cost $12,500. Assuming a steady rate of increase, what was the yearly rate of inflation in car prices over the 8-year period?
5.09%

Practice

Arithmetic Sequences

Find the nth term of each arithmetic sequence.

1. $a_1 = -5, d = 4, n = 9$

2. $a_1 = 13, d = -\dfrac{5}{2}, n = 29$

3. $a_1 = 3, d = -4, n = 6$

4. $a_1 = -5, d = \dfrac{1}{2}, n = 10$

Complete each statement.

5. 97 is the _____?____th term of $-3, 1, 5, 9, \cdots$.

6. -10 is the _____?____th term of $14, 12.5, 11, 9.5, \cdots$.

Find the indicated term in each arithmetic sequence.

7. a_{15} for $-3, 3, 9, \cdots$

8. a_{19} for $17, 12, 7, \cdots$

9. a_{26} for $1, \dfrac{7}{3}, \dfrac{11}{3}, \cdots$

10. a_{35} for $17, 16\dfrac{2}{3}, 16\dfrac{1}{3}, \cdots$

Find the missing terms in each arithmetic sequence.

11. 3, _____, _____, 20

12. _____, -10, _____, _____, _____, 14

13. 5, _____, _____, 27

14. _____, 4, _____, _____, _____, 29

15. How many multiples of 11 are there between 13 and 384?

Arithmetic Sequences

Find the nth term of each arithmetic sequence.

1. $a_1 = -5, d = 4, n = 9$
27

2. $a_1 = 13, d = -\frac{5}{2}, n = 29$
−57

3. $a_1 = 3, d = -4, n = 6$
−17

4. $a_1 = -5, d = \frac{1}{2}, n = 10$
$-\frac{1}{2}$

Complete each statement.

5. 97 is the ___?___th term of $-3, 1, 5, 9, \cdots$. **26**

6. -10 is the ___?___th term of $14, 12.5, 11, 9.5, \cdots$. **17**

Find the indicated term in each arithmetic sequence.

7. a_{15} for $-3, 3, 9, \cdots$
81

8. a_{19} for $17, 12, 7, \cdots$
−73

9. a_{26} for $1, \frac{7}{3}, \frac{11}{3}, \cdots$
$\frac{103}{3}$

10. a_{35} for $17, 16\frac{2}{3}, 16\frac{1}{3}, \cdots$
$\frac{17}{3}$

Find the missing terms in each arithmetic sequence.

11. $3, \_\_\_, \_\_\_, 20$
$8\frac{2}{3}, 14\frac{1}{3}$

12. $\_\_\_, -10, \_\_\_, \_\_\_, \_\_\_, 14$
−16, −4, 2, 8

13. $5, \_\_\_, \_\_\_, 27$
$12\frac{1}{3}, 19\frac{2}{3}$

14. $\_\_\_, 4, \_\_\_, \_\_\_, \_\_\_, 29$
$-2\frac{1}{4}, 10\frac{1}{4}, 16\frac{1}{2}, 22\frac{3}{4}$

15. How many multiples of 11 are there between 13 and 384?
33

NAME_____ DATE _____

Practice

Arithmetic Series

Find S_n for each arithmetic series described.

1. $a_1 = 16$, $a_n = 98$, $n = 13$

2. $a_1 = 13$, $d = -6$, $n = 21$

3. $d = -\frac{2}{3}$, $n = 16$, $a_n = 44$

4. $a_1 = -121$, $d = 3$, $a_n = 5$

Find the sum of each arithmetic series.

5. $5 + 7 + 9 + \cdots + 27$

6. $-4 + 1 + 6 + \cdots + 91$

7. $13 + 20 + 27 + \cdots + 272$

8. $89 + 86 + 83 + \cdots + 20$

9. $\sum_{k=3}^{8} (5k - 10)$

10. $\sum_{p=4}^{10} (2p + 1)$

11. $\sum_{n=1}^{6} (3n + 5)$

12. $\sum_{j=1}^{5} (9 - 4j)$

Find the first three terms of each arithmetic series.

13. $a_1 = 14$, $a_n = -85$, $S_n = -1207$

14. $n = 16$, $a_n = 15$, $S_n = -120$

Solve.

15. A display in a grocery store has 1 can on the top row, 2 cans on the 2nd row, 3 cans on the 3rd row, and so on. How many cans are needed to make 25 rows?

Practice

Arithmetic Series

Find S_n for each arithmetic series described.

1. $a_1 = 16$, $a_n = 98$, $n = 13$ **741**

2. $a_1 = 13$, $d = -6$, $n = 21$ **−987**

3. $d = -\frac{2}{3}$, $n = 16$, $a_n = 44$ **784**

4. $a_1 = -121$, $d = 3$, $a_n = 5$ **−2494**

Find the sum of each arithmetic series.

5. $5 + 7 + 9 + \cdots + 27$
192

6. $-4 + 1 + 6 + \cdots + 91$
870

7. $13 + 20 + 27 + \cdots + 272$
5415

8. $89 + 86 + 83 + \cdots + 20$
1308

9. $\sum_{k=3}^{8} (5k - 10)$
105

10. $\sum_{p=4}^{10} (2p + 1)$
105

11. $\sum_{n=1}^{6} (3n + 5)$
93

12. $\sum_{j=1}^{5} (9 - 4j)$
−15

Find the first three terms of each arithmetic series.

13. $a_1 = 14$, $a_n = -85$, $S_n = -1207$
14, 11, 8

14. $n = 16$, $a_n = 15$, $S_n = -120$
−30, −27, −24

Solve.

15. A display in a grocery store has 1 can on the top row, 2 cans on the 2nd row, 3 cans on the 3rd row, and so on. How many cans are needed to make 25 rows? **325**

NAME_____ DATE _____

Practice

Student Edition
Pages 662–669

Geometric Sequences

Find the first four terms of each geometric sequence.

1. $a_1 = -6, r = -\dfrac{2}{3}$

2. $a_1 = 2, r = \sqrt{3}$

3. $a_1 = -\dfrac{5}{2}, r = 2$

4. $a_1 = \sqrt{2}, r = \sqrt{3}$

Find the nth term of each geometric sequence.

5. $a_1 = 5, n = 4, r = 3$

6. $a_4 = 20, n = 6, r = -3$

7. $a_1 = -4, n = 6, r = -2$

8. $a_6 = 8, n = 12, r = \dfrac{1}{2}$

Solve.

9. Each foot of water screens out 60% of the light above. What percent of the light remains after passing through 5 feet of water?

Find the geometric means in each sequence. Then graph each sequence, using the x-axis for the number of the term and the y-axis for the term itself.

10. _____, _____, 2, _____, _____, 54

11. 32, _____, _____, _____, 162

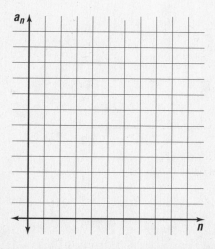

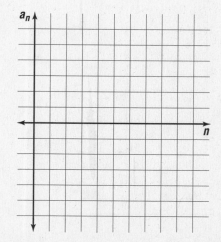

Geometric Sequences

Find the first four terms of each geometric sequence.

1. $a_1 = -6, r = -\dfrac{2}{3}$

   $-6, 4, -\dfrac{8}{3}, \dfrac{16}{9}$

2. $a_1 = 2, r = \sqrt{3}$

   $2, 2\sqrt{3}, 6, 6\sqrt{3}$

3. $a_1 = -\dfrac{5}{2}, r = 2$

   $-\dfrac{5}{2}, -5, -10, -20$

4. $a_1 = \sqrt{2}, r = \sqrt{3}$

   $\sqrt{2}, \sqrt{6}, 3\sqrt{2}, 3\sqrt{6}$

Find the nth term of each geometric sequence.

5. $a_1 = 5, n = 4, r = 3$ **135**

6. $a_4 = 20, n = 6, r = -3$ **180**

7. $a_1 = -4, n = 6, r = -2$ **128**

8. $a_6 = 8, n = 12, r = \dfrac{1}{2}$ **$\dfrac{1}{8}$**

Solve.

9. Each foot of water screens out 60% of the light above. What percent of the light remains after passing through 5 feet of water? **1.024%**

Find the geometric means in each sequence. Then graph each sequence, using the x-axis for the number of the term and the y-axis for the term itself.

10. _____, _____, 2, _____, _____, 54

    $\dfrac{2}{9}, \dfrac{2}{3}, 6, 18$

11. 32, _____, _____, _____, 162

    48, 72, 108, or −48, 72, −108

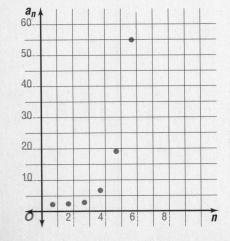

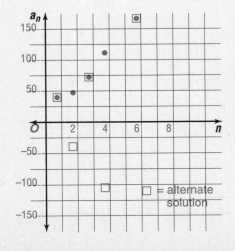

NAME_____ DATE _____

Practice

Geometric Series

Find the sum of each geometric series.

1. $160 + 80 + 40 + \cdots, n = 6$

2. $a_1 = 5, r = -\dfrac{1}{2}, n = 7$

3. $a_2 = \dfrac{-3}{8}, a_3 = \dfrac{1}{4}, n = 5$

4. $a_3 = 8, a_5 = 2, n = 6$

Express each series in sigma notation and find the sum.

5. $54 + 18 + 6 + 2 + \dfrac{2}{3} + \dfrac{2}{9}$

6. $16 - 24 + 36 - 54 + 81 - 121.5 + 182.25$

Find a_1 for each geometric series described.

7. $S_n = -55, r = -\dfrac{2}{3}, n = 5$

8. $S_n = 2457, a_n = 3072, r = -4$

Solve.

9. A pile driver drives a post 9 feet into the ground on its first hit. Each additional hit drives the post $\dfrac{2}{3}$ the distance of the prior hit. Find the total distance the post has been driven after 4 hits.

10. In problem 9, what is the greatest distance the pole could be driven into the ground?

11. Hugh Moore makes up a joke and tells it to his 5 closest friends on Sunday morning. Each of those friends tells his or her 5 closest friends on Monday morning, and so on. Assuming no duplication, how many people will have heard the joke by the end of Saturday?

NAME_____ DATE _____

Practice

Geometric Series

Find the sum of each geometric series.

1. $160 + 80 + 40 + \cdots, n = 6$ **315**

2. $a_1 = 5, r = -\dfrac{1}{2}, n = 7$ $\dfrac{215}{64}$

3. $a_2 = \dfrac{-3}{8}, a_3 = \dfrac{1}{4}, n = 5$ $\dfrac{58}{144}$

4. $a_3 = 8, a_5 = 2, n = 6$ **21 or 63**

Express each series in sigma notation and find the sum.

5. $54 + 18 + 6 + 2 + \dfrac{2}{3} + \dfrac{2}{9}$

$\displaystyle\sum_{n=1}^{6} 54\left(\dfrac{1}{3}\right)^{n-1}$

6. $16 - 24 + 36 - 54 + 81 - 121.5 + 182.25$

$\displaystyle\sum_{n=1}^{7} 16\left(-\dfrac{3}{2}\right)^{n-1}$

Find a_1 for each geometric series described.

7. $S_n = -55, r = -\dfrac{2}{3}, n = 5$ **−81**

8. $S_n = 2457, a_n = 3072, r = -4$ **−3**

Solve.

9. A pile driver drives a post 9 feet into the ground on its first hit. Each additional hit drives the post $\frac{2}{3}$ the distance of the prior hit. Find the total distance the post has been driven after 4 hits. $21\frac{2}{3}$ **ft**

10. In problem 9, what is the greatest distance the pole could be driven into the ground?   **27 ft**

11. Hugh Moore makes up a joke and tells it to his 5 closest friends on Sunday morning. Each of those friends tells his or her 5 closest friends on Monday morning, and so on. Assuming no duplication, how many people will have heard the joke by the end of Saturday?   **97,655; 97,656 if Hugh is included**

Algebra 2

NAME_____ DATE _____

Practice

Student Edition
Pages 676–682

Infinite Geometric Series

Find the sum of each infinite geometric series, if it exists.

1. $a_1 = 35, r = \dfrac{2}{7}$

2. $18 - 6 + 2 - \cdots$

3. $\dfrac{4}{25} + \dfrac{2}{5} + 1 + \cdots$

4. $6 + 4 + \dfrac{8}{3} + \cdots$

5. $10 + 1 + 0.1 + \cdots$

6. $2 + 6 + 18 + \cdots$

7. $a_1 = 26, r = \dfrac{1}{2}$

8. $a_1 = 108, r = -\dfrac{3}{4}$

9. $a_1 = 42, r = \dfrac{6}{5}$

10. $a_1 = 50, r = \dfrac{2}{5}$

Express each decimal as a rational number of the form $\dfrac{a}{b}$.

11. $0.4\overline{9}$

12. $0.\overline{164}$

13. $0.2\overline{8}$

14. $0.6\overline{41}$

Find the first three terms of each infinite geometric series.

15. $S = 64, r = -\dfrac{3}{4}$

16. $S = 625, r = \dfrac{1}{5}$

17. $S = 90, r = -\dfrac{1}{2}$

18. $S = 4, r = \dfrac{1}{3}$

Practice

Infinite Geometric Series

Find the sum of each infinite geometric series, if it exists.

1. $a_1 = 35, r = \frac{2}{7}$ **49**

2. $18 - 6 + 2 - \cdots$ $\frac{27}{2}$

3. $\frac{4}{25} + \frac{2}{5} + 1 + \cdots$ **does not exist**

4. $6 + 4 + \frac{8}{3} + \cdots$ **18**

5. $10 + 1 + 0.1 + \cdots$ $\frac{100}{9}$

6. $2 + 6 + 18 + \cdots$ **does not exist**

7. $a_1 = 26, r = \frac{1}{2}$ **52**

8. $a_1 = 108, r = -\frac{3}{4}$ $\frac{432}{7}$

9. $a_1 = 42, r = \frac{6}{5}$ **does not exist**

10. $a_1 = 50, r = \frac{2}{5}$ $\frac{250}{3}$

Express each decimal as a rational number of the form $\frac{a}{b}$.

11. $0.4\overline{9}$ **0.49 + 0.009 + 0.0009 + $\cdots$; $\frac{1}{2}$**

12. $0.\overline{164}$ **0.164 + 0.000164 + 0.000000164 + $\cdots$; $\frac{164}{999}$**

13. $0.2\overline{8}$ **0.28 + 0.008 + 0.0008 + $\cdots$; $\frac{13}{45}$**

14. $0.6\overline{41}$ **0.641 + 0.00041 + 0.0000041 + $\cdots$; $\frac{127}{198}$**

Find the first three terms of each infinite geometric series.

15. $S = 64, r = -\frac{3}{4}$ **112 − 84 + 63**

16. $S = 625, r = \frac{1}{5}$ **500 + 100 + 20**

17. $S = 90, r = -\frac{1}{2}$
    135 − 67.5 + 33.75

18. $S = 4, r = \frac{1}{3}$
    $\frac{8}{3} + \frac{8}{9} + \frac{8}{27}$

Practice

Recursion and Special Sequences

Find the first six terms of each sequence.

1. $f(0) = 1; f(1) = 1;$
   $f(n + 1) = 4 \cdot f(n - 1)$

2. $f(0) = 1; f(n + 1) = \frac{1}{2} + f(n)$

3. $f(0) = 1; f(1) = 1;$
   $f(n + 1) = 24 + f(n - 1)(-5)$

4. $f(0) = 2; f(n + 1) = f(n) + n - 2$

5. $f(0) = 4; f(n + 1) = (n - 1) + f(n)$

6. $f(1) = 1; f(2) = 1; f(n + 1) =$
   $f(n) - f(n - 1)$ where $n \geq 2$

Find the first three iterates of each function, using the given initial value.

7. $f(x) = 8 + 3x; x_0 = 1$

8. $f(x) = \frac{2}{2x - 1}; x_0 = -1$

9. $f(x) = 2x^2; x_0 = 5$

10. $f(x) = x(x + 1); x_0 = -5$

11. $f(x) = \frac{x - 1}{x}; x_0 = 10$

12. $f(x) = 10x + 2; x_0 = -1$

Practice

Recursion and Special Sequences

Find the first six terms of each sequence.

1. $f(0) = 1; f(1) = 1;$
   $f(n + 1) = 4 \cdot f(n - 1)$
   1, 1, 4, 4, 16, 16

2. $f(0) = 1; f(n + 1) = \frac{1}{2} + f(n)$
   1, $\frac{3}{2}$, 2, $\frac{5}{2}$, 3

3. $f(0) = 1; f(1) = 1;$
   $f(n + 1) = 24 + f(n - 1)(-5)$
   1, 1, 19, 19, −71, −71

4. $f(0) = 2; f(n + 1) = f(n) + n - 2$
   2, 1, 1, 2, 4, 7

5. $f(0) = 4; f(n + 1) = (n - 1) + f(n)$
   4, 3, 3, 4, 6, 9

6. $f(1) = 1; f(2) = 1; f(n + 1) =$
   $f(n) - f(n - 1)$ where $n \geq 2$
   1, 1, 0, −1, −1, 0

Find the first three iterates of each function, using the given initial value.

7. $f(x) = 8 + 3x; x_0 = 1$
   11, 41, 131

8. $f(x) = \dfrac{2}{2x - 1}; x_0 = -1$
   $-\dfrac{2}{3}$, $-\dfrac{6}{7}$, $-\dfrac{14}{19}$

9. $f(x) = 2x^2; x_0 = 5$
   50, 5000, 50,000,000

10. $f(x) = x(x + 1); x_0 = -5$
    20, 420, 176,820

11. $f(x) = \dfrac{x - 1}{x}; x_0 = 10$
    $\dfrac{9}{10}$, $-\dfrac{1}{9}$, 10

12. $f(x) = 10x + 2; x_0 = -1$
    − 8, −78, −778

Practice

Fractals

Draw the next stage of the fractal formed by replacing each segment with the pattern shown.

1.

2.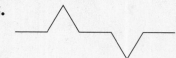

3. Refer to Sierpinski's Triangle on page 691 in the text.
   a. Draw the first four stages.

   b. If the perimeter of stage 1 is 24, find a recursive formula that describes how the perimeters of the shaded triangles change as the number of stages increase.

   c. Find the perimeter of the shaded triangles in stage 7.

NAME_____ DATE _____

Practice

Fractals

Draw the next stage of the fractal formed by replacing each segment with the pattern shown.

1.

2.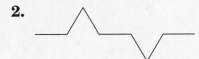

3. Refer to Sierpinski's Triangle on page 691 in the text.
   a. Draw the first four stages.

   b. If the perimeter of stage 1 is 24, find a recursive formula that describes how the perimeters of the shaded triangles change as the number of stages increase.

$$a_n = 24, \ a_{n+1} = \left(\frac{3}{2}\right) a_n$$

   c. Find the perimeter of the shaded triangles in stage 7.

$$a_7 = \left(\frac{3}{2}\right)(182.25) = 273.375$$

Practice

The Binomial Theorem

Use a calculator to evaluate each expression.

1. $7!$

2. $6!4!$

3. $\dfrac{8!}{6!2!}$

4. $\dfrac{8!}{5!3!}$

5. $(3! - 2!)!$

6. $\left(\dfrac{0! + 1! + 3!}{2!}\right)!$

Expand each binomial.

7. $(x + 3)^4$

8. $(2m - y)^4$

9. $(2x - y)^5$

10. $(r + 3)^5$

11. $(n + v)^8$

12. $(x - y)^7$

Find the indicated term of each expression.

13. fourth term of $(x - 3y)^6$

14. fifth term of $(2x - 1)^9$

15. seventh term of $(x + y)^{10}$

16. tenth term of $(2x + y)^{12}$

17. Find the sixth element in the tenth row of Pascal's triangle.

18. Find the ninth element in the fourteenth row of Pascal's triangle.

The Binomial Theorem

Use a calculator to evaluate each expression.

1. 7! 5040

2. 6!4! 17,280

3. $\frac{8!}{6!2!}$ 28

4. $\frac{8!}{5!3!}$ 56

5. $(3! - 2!)!$ 24

6. $\left(\frac{0! + 1! + 3!}{2!}\right)!$ 24

Expand each binomial.

7. $(x + 3)^4$
$x^4 + 12x^3 + 54x^2 + 108x + 81$

8. $(2m - y)^4$
$16m^4 - 32m^3y + 24m^2y^2 - 8my^3 + y^4$

9. $(2x - y)^5$ $32x^5 - 80x^4y + 80x^3y^2 - 40x^2y^3 + 10xy^4 - y^5$

10. $(r + 3)^5$ $r^5 + 15r^4 + 90r^3 + 270r^2 + 405r + 243$

11. $(n + v)^8$ $n^8 + 8n^7v + 28n^6v^2 + 56n^5v^3 + 70n^4v^4 + 56n^3v^5 + 28n^2v^6 + 8nv^7 + v^8$

12. $(x - y)^7$ $x^7 - 7x^6y + 21x^5y^2 - 35x^4y^3 + 35x^3y^4 - 21x^2y^5 + 7xy^6 - y^7$

Find the indicated term of each expression.

13. fourth term of $(x - 3y)^6$
$-540x^3y^3$

14. fifth term of $(2x - 1)^9$
$4032x^5$

15. seventh term of $(x + y)^{10}$
$210x^4y^6$

16. tenth term of $(2x + y)^{12}$
$1760x^3y^9$

17. Find the sixth element in the tenth row of Pascal's triangle.
126

18. Find the ninth element in the fourteenth row of Pascal's triangle. 1287

NAME_____ DATE _____

Practice

The Counting Principle

Solve.

1. A briefcase lock has 3 rotating cylinders, each containing 10 digits. How many numerical codes are possible?

2. A golf club manufacturer makes irons with 7 different shaft lengths, 3 different grips, 5 different lies, and 2 different club head materials. How many different combinations are offered?

3. There are five different routes that a commuter can take from her home to the office. In how many ways can she make a round trip if she uses a different route coming than going?

4. In how many ways can the 4 call letters of a radio station be arranged if the first letter must be W or K and no letters repeat?

5. How many 7-digit phone numbers can be formed if the first digit cannot be 0 or 1?

6. How many 7-digit phone numbers can be formed if the first digit cannot be 0 or 1 and if no digit can be repeated?

84

Practice

The Counting Principle

Solve.

1. A briefcase lock has 3 rotating cylinders, each containing 10 digits. How many numerical codes are possible? **1000**

2. A golf club manufacturer makes irons with 7 different shaft lengths, 3 different grips, 5 different lies, and 2 different club head materials. How many different combinations are offered? **210**

3. There are five different routes that a commuter can take from her home to the office. In how many ways can she make a round trip if she uses a different route coming than going? **20**

4. In how many ways can the 4 call letters of a radio station be arranged if the first letter must be W or K and no letters repeat? **27,600**

5. How many 7-digit phone numbers can be formed if the first digit cannot be 0 or 1? **8,000,000**

6. How many 7-digit phone numbers can be formed if the first digit cannot be 0 or 1 and if no digit can be repeated? **483,840**

Practice

Permutations

How many different ways can the letters of each word be arranged?

1. CANADA

2. ILLINI

3. ANNUALLY

4. MEMBERS

Evaluate each expression.

5. $\dfrac{8!}{6!}$

6. $P(8, 6)$

7. $\dfrac{P(7, 5)}{P(4, 3)}$

8. $\dfrac{P(6, 5)P(4, 4)}{P(5, 1)P(9, 2)}$

9. $\dfrac{P(8, 3)}{7!}$

10. $\dfrac{P(7, 4) \cdot P(5, 3)}{P(6, 5)}$

Solve.

11. A photographer is taking a picture of a bride and groom together with 6 attendants. How many ways can he arrange the 8 people in a line if the bridge and groom stand in the middle?

12. How many ways can 3 identical pen sets and 5 identical watches be given to 8 graduates if each receives one item?

13. How many ways can 4 charms be arranged on a bracelet that has no clasp?

14. How many ways can 4 charms be arranged on a bracelet that has a clasp?

15. How many ways can 5 men and 5 women be seated alternately at a round table?

16. How many ways can Laura and her 6 friends be seated around a table if Laura sits at the head of the table?

Permutations

How many different ways can the letters of each word be arranged?

1. CANADA **120**

2. ILLINI **60**

3. ANNUALLY **5040**

4. MEMBERS **1260**

Evaluate each expression.

5. $\frac{8!}{6!}$ **56**

6. $P(8, 6)$ **20,160**

7. $\frac{P(7, 5)}{P(4, 3)}$ **105**

8. $\frac{P(6, 5)P(4, 4)}{P(5, 1)P(9, 2)}$ **48**

9. $\frac{P(8, 3)}{7!}$ **$\frac{1}{15}$**

10. $\frac{P(7, 4) \cdot P(5, 3)}{P(6, 5)}$ **70**

Solve.

11. A photographer is taking a picture of a bride and groom together with 6 attendants. How many ways can he arrange the 8 people in a line if the bridge and groom stand in the middle? **1440**

12. How many ways can 3 identical pen sets and 5 identical watches be given to 8 graduates if each receives one item? **56**

13. How many ways can 4 charms be arranged on a bracelet that has no clasp? **3**

14. How many ways can 4 charms be arranged on a bracelet that has a clasp? **12**

15. How many ways can 5 men and 5 women be seated alternately at a round table? **1152**

16. How many ways can Laura and her 6 friends be seated around a table if Laura sits at the head of the table? **720**

NAME_____ DATE _____

Practice

Combinations

Evaluate each expression.

1. $C(8, 2)$

2. $C(11, 3)$

3. $C(20, 18)$

4. $C(9, 3) \cdot C(6, 2)$

Solve for x.

5. $C(x, 7) = C(x, 2)$

6. $C(11, 2) = C(x, 9)$

Solve.

7. How many 4-person bobsled teams can be chosen from a group of 9 athletes?

8. From a dessert cart in a fine restaurant, customers are allowed to pick 3 desserts from the 10 that are displayed. How many combinations are possible?

9. How many diagonals does a polygon with 12 sides have?

10. How many 5-sided polygons can be formed by joining any 5 of 11 points located on a circle?

An urn contains 8 white, 6 blue, and 9 red balls. How many ways can 6 balls be selected to meet each condition?

11. All balls are red.

12. Three are blue, 2 are white, and 1 is red.

13. Two are blue, and 4 are red.

14. Exactly 4 balls are white.

Practice

Combinations

Evaluate each expression.

1. $C(8, 2)$ **28**

2. $C(11, 3)$ **165**

3. $C(20, 18)$ **190**

4. $C(9, 3) \cdot C(6, 2)$ **1260**

Solve for x.

5. $C(x, 7) = C(x, 2)$ **9**

6. $C(11, 2) = C(x, 9)$ **11**

Solve.

7. How many 4-person bobsled teams can be chosen from a group of 9 athletes? **126**

8. From a dessert cart in a fine restaurant, customers are allowed to pick 3 desserts from the 10 that are displayed. How many combinations are possible? **120**

9. How many diagonals does a polygon with 12 sides have? **54**

10. How many 5-sided polygons can be formed by joining any 5 of 11 points located on a circle? **462**

An urn contains 8 white, 6 blue, and 9 red balls. How many ways can 6 balls be selected to meet each condition?

11. All balls are red. **84**

12. Three are blue, 2 are white, and 1 is red. **5040**

13. Two are blue, and 4 are red. **1890**

14. Exactly 4 balls are white. **7350**

Probability

State the odds of an event occurring, given the probability of the event.

1. $\frac{4}{11}$

2. $\frac{2}{3}$

3. $\frac{5}{99}$

4. $\frac{1}{1000}$

5. $\frac{5}{16}$

6. $\frac{3}{95}$

State the probability of an event occurring, given the odds of the event.

7. $\frac{2}{23}$

8. $\frac{3}{5}$

9. $\frac{4}{1}$

10. $\frac{9}{7}$

11. $\frac{11}{14}$

12. $\frac{1000}{1}$

A bag contains 1 green, 4 red, and 5 yellow balls. Two balls are selected at random. Find the probability of each selection.

13. $P(2 \text{ red})$

14. $P(1 \text{ red and } 1 \text{ yellow})$

15. $P(1 \text{ green and } 1 \text{ yellow})$

16. $P(2 \text{ green})$

A bank contains 3 pennies, 8 nickels, 4 dimes, and 10 quarters. Two coins are selected at random. Find the probability of each selection.

17. $P(2 \text{ pennies})$

18. $P(2 \text{ dimes})$

19. $P(1 \text{ nickel and } 1 \text{ dime})$

20. $P(1 \text{ quarter and } 1 \text{ penny})$

NAME_____ DATE _____

Practice

Probability

State the odds of an event occurring, given the probability of the event.

1. $\frac{4}{11}$ $\frac{4}{7}$

2. $\frac{2}{3}$ $\frac{2}{1}$

3. $\frac{5}{99}$ $\frac{5}{94}$

4. $\frac{1}{1000}$ $\frac{1}{999}$

5. $\frac{5}{16}$ $\frac{5}{11}$

6. $\frac{3}{95}$ $\frac{3}{92}$

State the probability of an event occurring, given the odds of the event.

7. $\frac{2}{23}$ $\frac{2}{25}$

8. $\frac{3}{5}$ $\frac{3}{8}$

9. $\frac{4}{1}$ $\frac{4}{5}$

10. $\frac{9}{7}$ $\frac{9}{16}$

11. $\frac{11}{14}$ $\frac{11}{25}$

12. $\frac{1000}{1}$ $\frac{1000}{1001}$

A bag contains 1 green, 4 red, and 5 yellow balls. Two balls are selected at random. Find the probability of each selection.

13. P(2 red) $\frac{2}{15}$

14. P(1 red and 1 yellow) $\frac{4}{9}$

15. P(1 green and 1 yellow) $\frac{1}{9}$

16. P(2 green) 0

A bank contains 3 pennies, 8 nickels, 4 dimes, and 10 quarters. Two coins are selected at random. Find the probability of each selection.

17. P(2 pennies) $\frac{1}{100}$

18. P(2 dimes) $\frac{1}{50}$

19. P(1 nickel and 1 dime) $\frac{8}{75}$

20. P(1 quarter and 1 penny) $\frac{1}{10}$

NAME_____ DATE _____

Practice

Multiplying Probabilities

There are 3 nickels, 2 dimes, and 5 quarters in a purse. Three coins are selected in succession at random.

1. Find the probability of selecting 1 nickel, 1 dime, and 1 quarter in that order without replacement.

2. Find the probability of selecting 1 nickel, 1 dime, and 1 quarter in that order with replacement.

3. Find the probability of selecting 1 nickel, 1 dime, and 1 quarter in any order with replacement.

4. Find the probability of selecting 1 nickel, 1 dime, and 1 quarter in any order without replacement.

A red, a green, and a yellow die are tossed. What is the probability that the following occurs?

5. All 3 dice show 4.

6. None of the 3 dice shows 4.

7. The red die shows an even number and the other 2 dice show different odd numbers.

8. All 3 dice show the same number.

From a standard deck of 52 cards, 2 cards are selected. What is the probability that the following occurs?

9. 2 black cards; selection without replacement.

10. 2 black cards; selection with replacement.

11. 1 red card and 1 spade in any order; selection without replacement.

12. 1 red card and 1 spade in that order; selection without replacement.

Practice

Multiplying Probabilities

There are 3 nickels, 2 dimes, and 5 quarters in a purse. Three coins are selected in succession at random.

1. Find the probability of selecting 1 nickel, 1 dime, and 1 quarter in that order without replacement. $\frac{1}{24}$

2. Find the probability of selecting 1 nickel, 1 dime, and 1 quarter in that order with replacement. $\frac{3}{100}$

3. Find the probability of selecting 1 nickel, 1 dime, and 1 quarter in any order with replacement. $\frac{9}{50}$

4. Find the probability of selecting 1 nickel, 1 dime, and 1 quarter in any order without replacement. $\frac{1}{4}$

A red, a green, and a yellow die are tossed. What is the probability that the following occurs?

5. All 3 dice show 4. $\frac{1}{216}$

6. None of the 3 dice shows 4. $\frac{125}{216}$

7. The red die shows an even number and the other 2 dice show different odd numbers. $\frac{1}{12}$

8. All 3 dice show the same number. $\frac{1}{36}$

From a standard deck of 52 cards, 2 cards are selected. What is the probability that the following occurs?

9. 2 black cards; selection without replacement. $\frac{25}{102}$

10. 2 black cards; selection with replacement. $\frac{1}{4}$

11. 1 red card and 1 spade in any order; selection without replacement. $\frac{13}{51}$

12. 1 red card and 1 spade in that order; selection without replacement. $\frac{13}{102}$

Practice

Adding Probabilities

An urn contains 7 white marbles and 5 blue marbles. Four marbles are selected without replacement. What is the probability that the following occurs?

1. all white or all blue

2. exactly 3 white

3. at least 3 white

4. exactly 3 white or exactly 3 blue

Two cards are drawn from a standard deck of 52 cards. What is the probability that the following occurs?

5. 2 spades

6. 2 spades or 2 red cards

7. 2 red cards or 2 jacks

8. 2 spades or 2 face cards

Three dice are tossed. What is the probability that the following occurs?

9. only two 5s

10. at least two 5s

11. three 5s

12. no 5s

Practice

Adding Probabilities

An urn contains 7 white marbles and 5 blue marbles. Four marbles are selected without replacement. What is the probability that the following occurs?

1. all white or all blue $\dfrac{8}{99}$

2. exactly 3 white $\dfrac{35}{99}$

3. at least 3 white $\dfrac{14}{33}$

4. exactly 3 white or exactly 3 blue $\dfrac{49}{99}$

Two cards are drawn from a standard deck of 52 cards. What is the probability that the following occurs?

5. 2 spades $\dfrac{1}{17}$

6. 2 spades or 2 red cards $\dfrac{31}{102}$

7. 2 red cards or 2 jacks $\dfrac{55}{221}$

8. 2 spades or 2 face cards $\dfrac{47}{442}$

Three dice are tossed. What is the probability that the following occurs?

9. only two 5s $\dfrac{5}{72}$

10. at least two 5s $\dfrac{2}{27}$

11. three 5s $\dfrac{1}{216}$

12. no 5s $\dfrac{125}{216}$

Algebra 2

Practice

Binomial Experiments and Simulations

Six coins are tossed. What is the probability that the following occurs?

1. 3 heads and 3 tails

2. at least 4 heads

3. 2 heads or 5 tails

4. all heads or all tails

The probability of Chris making a free throw is $\frac{2}{3}$. If she shoots five times, what is the probability of the following?

5. all missed

6. all made

7. exactly 4 made

8. at least 3 made

When Mary and Sam play a certain board game, the probability that Mary will win a game is $\frac{3}{4}$. If they play five games, find the probability of each event.

9. Sam wins only once.

10. Mary wins exactly twice.

11. Sam wins at least two games.

12. Mary wins at least three games.

12-7

Practice

Binomial Experiments and Simulations

Six coins are tossed. What is the probability that the following occurs?

1. 3 heads and 3 tails $\frac{5}{16}$

2. at least 4 heads $\frac{11}{32}$

3. 2 heads or 5 tails $\frac{21}{64}$

4. all heads or all tails $\frac{1}{32}$

The probability of Chris making a free throw is $\frac{2}{3}$. If she shoots five times, what is the probability of the following?

5. all missed $\frac{1}{243}$

6. all made $\frac{32}{243}$

7. exactly 4 made $\frac{80}{243}$

8. at least 3 made $\frac{64}{81}$

When Mary and Sam play a certain board game, the probability that Mary will win a game is $\frac{3}{4}$. If they play five games, find the probability of each event.

9. Sam wins only once. $\frac{405}{1024}$

10. Mary wins exactly twice. $\frac{45}{512}$

11. Sam wins at least two games. $\frac{47}{128}$

12. Mary wins at least three games. $\frac{459}{512}$

Algebra 2

Practice

Sampling and Testing Hypotheses

Determine whether each situation represents a random sampling. Write yes or no and explain.

1. You are calling every twentieth name in the telephone directory to determine if people own or rent their homes in your community.

2. A school's librarian was concerned because not many students were using the library. To find out why, she gave a questionnaire to every student entering the library.

3. Overall performance of tires is tested on highways.

4. Presidential election results are predicted by polling people in every third home in different neighborhoods of your community.

Find the margin of sampling error in Exercises 5–7. Explain what it indicates about the results.

5. According to a poll of 500 teenagers, 43% said that they use a personal computer at home.

6. A survey of 605 people, ages 13–33, showed that 68% trust their parents more than their best friends to tell them the truth.

7. A study by the University of Illinois in 1995 showed a 10% increase in productivity of 75 employees who wore headsets and listened to the music of their choice while they were working.

Sampling and Testing Hypotheses

Determine whether each situation represents a random sampling. Write yes or no and explain.

1. You are calling every twentieth name in the telephone directory to determine if people own or rent their homes in your community.
   Yes; this is a random sample since most people in the community are listed in telephone directories.

2. A school's librarian was concerned because not many students were using the library. To find out why, she gave a questionnaire to every student entering the library.
   No; she is only polling the students who are coming to the library—not all of the students in the school.

3. Overall performance of tires is tested on highways.
   No; overall tire performance needs to be tested on all types of surface areas.

4. Presidential election results are predicted by polling people in every third home in different neighborhoods of your community.
   Yes; different neighborhoods will result in a good range of results.

Find the margin of sampling error in Exercises 5–7. Explain what it indicates about the results.

5. According to a poll of 500 teenagers, 43% said that they use a personal computer at home.
   ME = 4.4% There is a 95% probability that 38.6–47.4% of the students use a personal computer.

6. A survey of 605 people, ages 13–33, showed that 68% trust their parents more than their best friends to tell them the truth.
   ME = 3.8% There is a 95% probability that 64.2–71.8% of 13–33 year-olds trust their parents more than their best friends.

7. A study by the University of Illinois in 1995 showed a 10% increase in productivity of 75 employees who wore headsets and listened to the music of their choice while they were working.
   ME = 6.9% There is a 95% probability that there was a 3.1–16.9% increase in productivity of the employees who wore headsets and listened to music while they were working.

An Introduction to Trigonometry

Using the triangle shown, write an equation involving sin, cos, or tan that can be used to find the missing measure. Then solve the equation. Round measures of sides to the nearest tenth.

1. If $A = 20°$ and $c = 32$, find a.

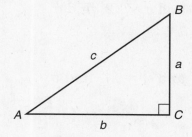

2. If $A = 49°$ and $a = 17$, find b.

3. If $A = 27.3°$ and $a = 7$, find c.

4. If $a = 19.2$ and $A = 63.4°$, find b.   5. If $a = 28$ and $B = 41°$, find c.

Solve each right triangle. Assume that C represents the right angle and c is the hypotenuse. Round measures of sides and angles to the nearest tenth.

6. $a = 12, A = 35°$ 7. $b = 25, B = 71°$

8. $a = 4, b = 7$ 9. $b = 52, c = 95$

Solve each problem. Round measures of lengths to the nearest tenth.

10. An airplane is directly above a beacon that is 10,000 feet from an airport control tower. The angle of depression from the plane to the base of the control tower is 6°. How high above the beacon is the plane?

11. John views the top of a water tower at an angle of elevation of 36°. He walks 120 meters in a straight line toward the tower. Then he sights the top of the tower at an angle of elevation of 51°. How far is John from the base of the tower?

NAME _____ DATE _____

Practice

An Introduction to Trigonometry

Using the triangle shown, write an equation involving sin, cos, or tan that can be used to find the missing measure. Then solve the equation. Round measures of sides to the nearest tenth.

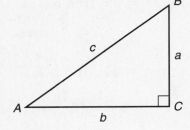

1. If $A = 20°$ and $c = 32$, find a.

   $\sin 20° = \dfrac{a}{32}$; **10.9**

2. If $A = 49°$ and $a = 17$, find b.

   $\tan 49° = \dfrac{17}{b}$; **14.8**

3. If $A = 27.3°$ and $a = 7$, find c.

   $\sin 27.3° = \dfrac{7}{c}$; **15.3**

4. If $a = 19.2$ and $A = 63.4°$, find b.

   $\tan 63.4° = \dfrac{19.2}{b}$; **9.6**

5. If $a = 28$ and $B = 41°$, find c.

   $\cos 41° = \dfrac{28}{c}$; **37.1**

Solve each right triangle. Assume that C represents the right angle and c is the hypotenuse. Round measures of sides and angles to the nearest tenth.

6. $a = 12, A = 35°$
   $B = 55°, b = 17.1, c = 20.9$

7. $b = 25, B = 71°$
   $A = 19°, a = 8.6, c = 26.4$

8. $a = 4, b = 7$
   $A = 29.6°, B = 60.3°, c = 8.1$

9. $b = 52, c = 95$
   $a = 79.5, A = 56.8°, B = 33.2°$

Solve each problem. Round measures of lengths to the nearest tenth.

10. An airplane is directly above a beacon that is 10,000 feet from an airport control tower. The angle of depression from the plane to the base of the control tower is 6°. How high above the beacon is the plane?
    1051.0 feet

11. John views the top of a water tower at an angle of elevation of 36°. He walks 120 meters in a straight line toward the tower. Then he sights the top of the tower at an angle of elevation of 51°. How far is John from the base of the tower?
    171.5 meters

Algebra 2

Angles and Their Measure

Change each degree measure to radian measure.

1. $18°$

2. $-72°$

3. $-820°$

4. $6°$

5. $-250°$

6. $870°$

7. $347°$

8. $-165°$

9. $2\pi°$

10. $-\frac{4}{3}\pi°$

Change each radian measure to degree measure.

11. 4π

12. $\frac{5}{2}\pi$

13. $\frac{-7}{9}\pi$

14. $2\frac{3}{5}\pi$

15. $\frac{13}{30}\pi$

16. $-\frac{4}{7}\pi$

17. 4

18. $-\frac{5}{2}$

19. $\frac{5\pi}{4}$

20. $\frac{3\pi}{16}$

Angles and Their Measure

Change each degree measure to radian measure.

1. $18°$ $\dfrac{\pi}{10}$

2. $-72°$ $-\dfrac{2\pi}{5}$

3. $-820°$ $-\dfrac{41\pi}{9}$

4. $6°$ $\dfrac{\pi}{30}$

5. $-250°$ $-\dfrac{25\pi}{18}$

6. $870°$ $\dfrac{29\pi}{6}$

7. $347°$ $\dfrac{347\pi}{180}$

8. $-165°$ $-\dfrac{11\pi}{12}$

9. $2\pi°$ $\dfrac{\pi^2}{90}$

10. $-\dfrac{4}{3}\pi°$ $-\dfrac{\pi^2}{135}$

Change each radian measure to degree measure.

11. 4π $720°$

12. $\dfrac{5}{2}\pi$ $450°$

13. $\dfrac{-7}{9}\pi$ $-140°$

14. $2\dfrac{3}{5}\pi$ $468°$

15. $\dfrac{13}{30}\pi$ $78°$

16. $-\dfrac{4}{7}\pi$ $-102.86°$

17. 4 $\dfrac{720°}{\pi} \approx 229.18$

18. $-\dfrac{5}{2}$ $-\dfrac{450°}{\pi} \approx -143.24$

19. $\dfrac{5\pi}{4}$ $225°$

20. $\dfrac{3\pi}{16}$ $33.75°$

NAME _____ DATE _____

Practice

Student Edition
Pages 786–791

Trigonometric Functions of General Angles

Find the exact value of each trigonometric function.

1. $\tan 135°$

2. $\sec \dfrac{\pi}{6}$

3. $\csc -\dfrac{\pi}{6}$

4. $\cot 210°$

5. $\sec 210°$

6. $\csc\left(-\dfrac{3}{4}\pi\right)$

7. $\tan \dfrac{5}{3}\pi$

8. $\cot(-405°)$

9. $\csc(-390°)$

10. $\sec 270°$

11. $\cot(-87\pi)$

12. $\tan \dfrac{13}{6}\pi$

13. $\sec(-225°)$

14. $\csc 4\dfrac{2}{3}\pi$

15. $\tan(-720°)$

16. $\cot(-90°)$

17. $\sec 330°$

18. $\csc -\dfrac{11\pi}{6}$

19. $\cot \dfrac{9\pi}{4}$

20. $\tan -\dfrac{3\pi}{4}$

NAME_____ DATE _____

Practice

Trigonometric Functions of General Angles

Find the exact value of each trigonometric function.

1. $\tan 135°$ -1

2. $\sec \dfrac{\pi}{6}$ $\dfrac{2\sqrt{3}}{3}$

3. $\csc -\dfrac{\pi}{6}$ -2

4. $\cot 210°$ $\sqrt{3}$

5. $\sec 210°$ $-\dfrac{2\sqrt{3}}{3}$

6. $\csc\left(-\dfrac{3}{4}\pi\right)$ $-\sqrt{2}$

7. $\tan \dfrac{5}{3}\pi$ $-\sqrt{3}$

8. $\cot(-405°)$ -1

9. $\csc(-390°)$ -2

10. $\sec 270°$ **undefined**

11. $\cot(-87\pi)$ **undefined**

12. $\tan \dfrac{13}{6}\pi$ $\dfrac{\sqrt{3}}{3}$

13. $\sec(-225°)$ $-\sqrt{2}$

14. $\csc 4\dfrac{2}{3}\pi$ $\dfrac{2\sqrt{3}}{3}$

15. $\tan(-720°)$ 0

16. $\cot(-90°)$ 0

17. $\sec 330°$ $\dfrac{2\sqrt{3}}{3}$

18. $\csc -\dfrac{11\pi}{6}$ 2

19. $\cot \dfrac{9\pi}{4}$ 1

20. $\tan -\dfrac{3\pi}{4}$ 1

Law of Sines

Find the area of each triangle described below. Round answers to the nearest tenth.

1. $a = 9$, $b = 11$, $C = 46°$

2. $a = 12$, $c = 15$, $B = 58°$

3. $b = 9$, $c = 9$, $A = 40°$

4. $a = 12.6$, $b = 8.9$, $C = 32°$

5. $a = 14.9$, $c = 18.6$, $B = 27°$

6. $b = 19.4$, $c = 8.6$, $A = 34°$

7. $a = 9$, $b = 7$, $C = 26.1°$

8. $b = 12$, $c = 19$, $A = 46.4°$

9. $a = 12$, $c = 14$, $B = 56.5°$

10. $b = 12$, $c = 14$, $A = 17.4°$

Solve each triangle described below. Round measures of sides and angles to the nearest tenth.

11. $A = 50°$, $B = 30°$, $c = 9$

12. $a = 12$, $A = 56°$, $B = 38°$

13. $a = 14$, $b = 18$, $A = 36.8°$

14. $b = 20$, $c = 25$, $C = 70.2°$

15. $a = 25$, $b = 30$, $A = 46.3°$

16. $a = 40$, $A = 80.2°$, $C = 14.2°$

17. $A = 80°$, $C = 40°$, $c = 30$

18. $c = 42$, $b = 56$, $C = 43.5°$

19. $b = 13$, $B = 46.6°$, $C = 112°$

20. $A = 110°$, $a = 20$, $b = 8$

Practice

Law of Sines

Find the area of each triangle described below. Round answers to the nearest tenth.

1. $a = 9$, $b = 11$, $C = 46°$
35.6

2. $a = 12$, $c = 15$, $B = 58°$
76.3

3. $b = 9$, $c = 9$, $A = 40°$
26.0

4. $a = 12.6$, $b = 8.9$, $C = 32°$
29.7

5. $a = 14.9$, $c = 18.6$, $B = 27°$
62.9

6. $b = 19.4$, $c = 8.6$, $A = 34°$
46.7

7. $a = 9$, $b = 7$, $C = 26.1°$
13.9

8. $b = 12$, $c = 19$, $A = 46.4°$
82.6

9. $a = 12$, $c = 14$, $B = 56.5°$
70.0

10. $b = 12$, $c = 14$, $A = 17.4°$
25.1

Solve each triangle described below. Round measures of sides and angles to the nearest tenth.

11. $A = 50°$, $B = 30°$, $c = 9$
$C = 100°$, $a = 7.0$, $b = 4.6$

12. $a = 12$, $A = 56°$, $B = 38°$
$C = 86°$, $b = 8.9$, $c = 14.4$

13. $a = 14$, $b = 18$, $A = 36.8°$
$B = 50.4°$, $C = 92.8°$, $c = 23.3$

14. $b = 20$, $c = 25$, $C = 70.2°$
$B = 48.8°$, $A = 61.0°$, $a = 23.2$

15. $a = 25$, $b = 30$, $A = 46.3°$
$B = 60.2°$, $C = 73.5°$, $c = 33.2$

16. $a = 40$, $A = 80.2°$, $C = 14.2°$
$B = 85.6°$, $b = 40.5$, $c = 10.0$

17. $A = 80°$, $C = 40°$, $c = 30$
$B = 60°$, $a = 46.0$, $b = 40.4$

18. $c = 42$, $b = 56$, $C = 43.5°$
$B = 66.6°$, $A = 69.9°$, $a = 57.3$

19. $b = 13$, $B = 46.6°$, $C = 112°$
$A = 21.4°$, $a = 6.5$, $c = 16.6$

20. $A = 110°$, $a = 20$, $b = 8$
$B = 22.1°$, $C = 47.9°$, $c = 15.8$

Law of Cosines

Solve each triangle described below. Round measures of sides and angles to the nearest tenth.

1. $a = 12, b = 7, C = 80°$

2. $a = 16, b = 20, C = 54°$

3. $A = 78.3°, b = 7, c = 11$

4. $B = 71°, c = 6, a = 11$

5. $a = 8, b = 6, c = 9$

6. $a = 16.4, b = 21.1, c = 18.5$

7. $a = 4, b = 5, c = 8$

8. $a = 4, b = 3, c = 6$

9. $A = 23°, b = 10, c = 12$

10. $C = 35°, b = 24, a = 18$

11. Two motorists start at the same point and travel in two straight courses. The courses diverge by 95°. If one is traveling at 50 mph and the other is traveling at 65 mph, how far apart will they be after 4 hours?

12. In problem 11, when will the motorists be 400 miles apart?

Law of Cosines

Solve each triangle described below. Round measures of sides and angles to the nearest tenth.

1. $a = 12$, $b = 7$, $C = 80°$
  $c = 12.8$, $A = 67.4°$,
  $B = 32.6°$

2. $a = 16$, $b = 20$, $C = 54°$
  $c = 16.7$, $A = 50.7°$,
  $B = 75.2°$

3. $A = 78.3°$, $b = 7$, $c = 11$
  $a = 11.8$, $B = 35.5°$,
  $C = 66.2°$

4. $B = 71°$, $c = 6$, $a = 11$
  $b = 10.7$, $C = 32.0°$,
  $A = 77°$

5. $a = 8$, $b = 6$, $c = 9$
  $A = 60.6°$, $B = 40.8°$,
  $C = 78.6°$

6. $a = 16.4$, $b = 21.1$, $c = 18.5$
  $A = 48.4°$, $B = 74.2°$,
  $C = 57.4°$

7. $a = 4$, $b = 5$, $c = 8$
  $A = 24.1°$, $B = 30.7°$,
  $C = 125.2°$

8. $a = 4$, $b = 3$, $c = 6$
  $A = 36.3°$, $B = 26.4°$,
  $C = 117.3°$

9. $A = 23°$, $b = 10$, $c = 12$
  $a = 4.8$, $B = 54.5°$,
  $C = 102.5°$

10. $C = 35°$, $b = 24$, $a = 18$
  $c = 13.9$, $B = 82°$,
  $A = 63.0°$

11. Two motorists start at the same point and travel in two straight courses. The courses diverge by 95°. If one is traveling at 50 mph and the other is traveling at 65 mph, how far apart will they be after 4 hours?
341.6 miles

12. In problem 11, when will the motorists be 400 miles apart?
4.7 hours

Circular Functions

Find the value of each function.

1. $\cos \dfrac{7\pi}{4}$

2. $\sin -30°$

3. $\sin\left(-\dfrac{2}{3}\pi\right)$

4. $\cos(-330°)$

5. $\cos 600°$

6. $\sin \dfrac{9}{2}\pi$

7. $\cos 187\pi$

8. $\cos\left(-\dfrac{11}{4}\pi\right)$

9. $\sin(-225°)$

10. $\sin 870°$

Practice

Circular Functions

Find the value of each function.

1. $\cos \dfrac{7\pi}{4}$ $\dfrac{\sqrt{2}}{2}$

2. $\sin -30°$ $-\dfrac{1}{2}$

3. $\sin\left(-\dfrac{2}{3}\pi\right)$ $-\dfrac{\sqrt{3}}{2}$

4. $\cos(-330°)$ $\dfrac{\sqrt{3}}{2}$

5. $\cos 600°$ $-\dfrac{1}{2}$

6. $\sin \dfrac{9}{2}\pi$ 1

7. $\cos 187\pi$ -1

8. $\cos\left(-\dfrac{11}{4}\pi\right)$ $-\dfrac{\sqrt{2}}{2}$

9. $\sin(-225°)$ $\dfrac{\sqrt{2}}{2}$

10. $\sin 870°$ $\dfrac{1}{2}$

Practice

Inverse Trigonometric Functions

Find each value.

1. $\text{Cos}^{-1}\left(-\dfrac{\sqrt{3}}{2}\right)$

2. $\text{Sin}^{-1}\left(-\dfrac{\sqrt{2}}{2}\right)$

3. $\text{Arctan}\left(-\dfrac{\sqrt{3}}{3}\right)$

4. $\text{Arccos } 1$

5. $\sin\left(\text{Sin}^{-1}\dfrac{3}{8}\right)$

6. $\cos\left(\text{Sin}^{-1}-\dfrac{3}{5}\right)$

7. $\tan\left(\text{Cos}^{-1}-\dfrac{\sqrt{3}}{2}\right)$

8. $\sec\left(\text{Cos}^{-1}\dfrac{2}{9}\right)$

9. $\csc(\text{Arctan } -1)$

10. $\cot\left(\text{Arcsin }\dfrac{12}{13}\right)$

11. $\text{Sin}^{-1}\left(\cos\dfrac{\pi}{3}\right)$

12. $\text{Cos}^{-1}\left(\tan\dfrac{3}{4}\pi\right)$

13. $\sin\left(2\,\text{Cos}^{-1}\dfrac{15}{17}\right)$

14. $\cos\left(2\,\text{Sin}^{-1}\dfrac{\sqrt{3}}{2}\right)$

15. $\sin\left(\text{Arctan}\dfrac{\sqrt{3}}{3}\right)$

16. $\text{Sin}^{-1}(\tan 45°)$

17. $\text{Cos}^{-1}\left(\text{Sin}\dfrac{\pi}{6}\right)$

18. $\sec\left(\text{Cos}^{-1}\dfrac{4}{5}\right)$

19. $\csc\left(\text{Sin}^{-1}\dfrac{9}{10}\right)$

20. $\cot(\text{Sin}^{-1} 0)$

NAME_____ DATE _____

Practice

Inverse Trigonometric Functions

Find each value.

1. $\cos^{-1}\left(-\frac{\sqrt{3}}{2}\right)$ **150°**

2. $\sin^{-1}\left(-\frac{\sqrt{2}}{2}\right)$ **−45°**

3. $\arctan\left(-\frac{\sqrt{3}}{3}\right)$ **−30°**

4. $\arccos 1$ **0°**

5. $\sin\left(\sin^{-1}\frac{3}{8}\right)$ **$\frac{3}{8}$**

6. $\cos\left(\sin^{-1}-\frac{3}{5}\right)$ **$\frac{4}{5}$**

7. $\tan\left(\cos^{-1}-\frac{\sqrt{3}}{2}\right)$ **$-\frac{\sqrt{3}}{3}$**

8. $\sec\left(\cos^{-1}\frac{2}{9}\right)$ **$\frac{9}{2}$**

9. $\csc(\arctan -1)$ **$-\sqrt{2}$**

10. $\cot\left(\arcsin\frac{12}{13}\right)$ **$\frac{5}{12}$**

11. $\sin^{-1}\left(\cos\frac{\pi}{3}\right)$ **30°**

12. $\cos^{-1}\left(\tan\frac{3}{4}\pi\right)$ **180°**

13. $\sin\left(2\cos^{-1}\frac{15}{17}\right)$ **$\frac{240}{289}$**

14. $\cos\left(2\sin^{-1}\frac{\sqrt{3}}{2}\right)$ **$-\frac{1}{2}$**

15. $\sin\left(\arctan\frac{\sqrt{3}}{3}\right)$ **$\frac{1}{2}$**

16. $\sin^{-1}(\tan 45°)$ **$\frac{\pi}{2}$ or 90°**

17. $\cos^{-1}\left(\sin\frac{\pi}{6}\right)$ **$\frac{\pi}{3}$ or 60°**

18. $\sec\left(\cos^{-1}\frac{4}{5}\right)$ **$\frac{5}{4}$**

19. $\csc\left(\sin^{-1}\frac{9}{10}\right)$ **$\frac{10}{9}$**

20. $\cot(\sin^{-1}0)$ **undefined**

Algebra 2

14-1

Practice

Graphing Trigonometric Functions

State the amplitude (if it exists) and period of each function.

1. $y = -4 \sin \theta$

2. $y = \cos 5\theta$

3. $y = \frac{1}{2} \sin \frac{3}{8}\theta$

4. $2y = -6 \cos 4\theta$

Graph each function.

5. $y = \sec 5\theta$

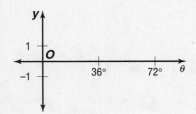

6. $y = \csc \frac{3}{4}\theta$

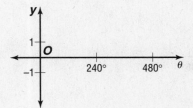

7. $y = \cot \frac{1}{2}\theta$

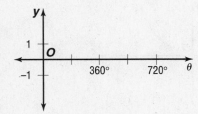

8. $y = \tan 10\theta$

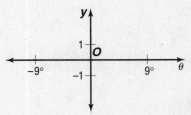

9. $y = 3 \csc 6\theta$

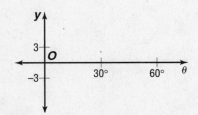

10. $y = \frac{1}{2} \sec 4\theta$

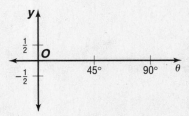

NAME_____ DATE _____

Practice

Graphing Trigonometric Functions

State the amplitude (if it exists) and period of each function.

1. $y = -4 \sin \theta$ **4; 360° or 2π**

2. $y = \cos 5\theta$ **1; 72° or $\frac{2\pi}{5}$**

3. $y = \frac{1}{2} \sin \frac{3}{8}\theta$ **$\frac{1}{2}$; 960° or $\frac{16\pi}{3}$**

4. $2y = -6 \cos 4\theta$ **3; 90° or $\frac{\pi}{2}$**

Graph each function.

5. $y = \sec 5\theta$

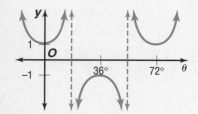

6. $y = \csc \frac{3}{4}\theta$

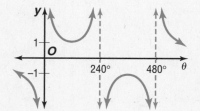

7. $y = \cot \frac{1}{2}\theta$

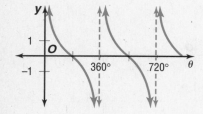

8. $y = \tan 10\theta$

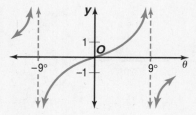

9. $y = 3 \csc 6\theta$

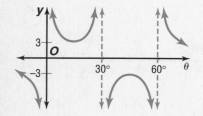

10. $y = \frac{1}{2} \sec 4\theta$

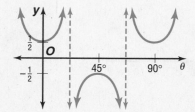

Algebra 2

Trigonometric Identities

Solve for values of θ between 0° and 90°.

1. If $\cos \theta = \dfrac{5}{13}$, find $\sin \theta$.

2. If $\sec \theta = 2$, find $\tan \theta$.

3. If $\cot \theta = \dfrac{1}{2}$, find $\sin \theta$.

4. If $\tan \theta = \dfrac{2}{5}$, find $\cot \theta$.

Solve for values of θ between 180° and 270°.

5. If $\sin \theta = -\dfrac{15}{17}$, find $\sec \theta$.

6. If $\tan \theta = 4$, find $\sec \theta$.

7. If $\csc \theta = -\dfrac{3}{2}$, find $\cot \theta$.

8. If $\sin \theta = -\dfrac{2}{9}$, find $\csc \theta$.

Solve for values of θ between 270° and 360°.

9. If $\cos \theta = \dfrac{3}{10}$, find $\cot \theta$.

10. If $\tan \theta = -\dfrac{1}{2}$, find $\sin \theta$.

11. If $\csc \theta = -8$, find $\sec \theta$.

12. If $\sec \theta = 3$, find $\cot \theta$.

Trigonometric Identities

Solve for values of θ between 0° and 90°.

1. If $\cos \theta = \frac{5}{13}$, find $\sin \theta$. $\frac{12}{13}$

2. If $\sec \theta = 2$, find $\tan \theta$. $\sqrt{3}$

3. If $\cot \theta = \frac{1}{2}$, find $\sin \theta$. $\frac{2\sqrt{5}}{5}$

4. If $\tan \theta = \frac{2}{5}$, find $\cot \theta$. $\frac{5}{2}$

Solve for values of θ between 180° and 270°.

5. If $\sin \theta = -\frac{15}{17}$, find $\sec \theta$. $-\frac{17}{8}$

6. If $\tan \theta = 4$, find $\sec \theta$. $-\sqrt{17}$

7. If $\csc \theta = -\frac{3}{2}$, find $\cot \theta$. $\frac{\sqrt{5}}{2}$

8. If $\sin \theta = -\frac{2}{9}$, find $\csc \theta$. $-\frac{9}{2}$

Solve for values of θ between 270° and 360°.

9. If $\cos \theta = \frac{3}{10}$, find $\cot \theta$. $-\frac{3\sqrt{91}}{91}$

10. If $\tan \theta = -\frac{1}{2}$, find $\sin \theta$. $-\frac{\sqrt{5}}{5}$

11. If $\csc \theta = -8$, find $\sec \theta$. $\frac{8\sqrt{7}}{21}$

12. If $\sec \theta = 3$, find $\cot \theta$. $-\frac{\sqrt{2}}{4}$

Verifying Trigonometric Identities

Verify that each of the following is an identity.

1. $(1 + \sin\theta)(1 - \sin\theta) = \dfrac{1}{\sec^2\theta}$

2. $\cos^2 x \cot^2 x = \cot^2 x - \cos^2 x$

3. $\tan^4 w + 2\tan^2 w + 1 = \sec^4 w$

4. $\sin^2 x(\csc^2 x + \sec^2 x) = \sec^2 x$

5. $\dfrac{\sin x + \cos x}{1 - \sin x} = \dfrac{1 + \cot x}{\csc x - 1}$

6. $\dfrac{1 - \tan x}{1 + \tan x} = \dfrac{\cot x - 1}{\cot x + 1}$

NAME_____ DATE _____

Practice

Verifying Trigonometric Identities

Verify that each of the following is an identity.

1. $(1 + \sin\theta)(1 - \sin\theta) = \dfrac{1}{\sec^2\theta}$

$$(1 + \sin\theta)(1 - \sin\theta) \overset{?}{=} \dfrac{1}{\sec^2\theta}$$
$$1 - \sin^2\theta \overset{?}{=} \cos^2\theta$$
$$\cos^2\theta = \cos^2\theta$$

2. $\cos^2 x \cot^2 x = \cot^2 x - \cos^2 x$

$$\cos^2 x \cot^2 x \overset{?}{=} \cot^2 x - \cos^2 x$$
$$\cos^2 x \cdot \dfrac{\cos^2 x}{\sin^2 x} \overset{?}{=} \dfrac{\cos^2 x}{\sin^2 x} - \dfrac{\cos^2 x \sin^2 x}{\sin^2 x}$$
$$\dfrac{\cos^4 x}{\sin^2 x} \overset{?}{=} \dfrac{\cos^2 x(1 - \sin^2 x)}{\sin^2 x}$$
$$\dfrac{\cos^4 x}{\sin^2 x} = \dfrac{\cos^4 x}{\sin^2 x}$$

3. $\tan^4 w + 2\tan^2 w + 1 = \sec^4 w$

$$\tan^4 w + 2\tan^2 w + 1 \overset{?}{=} \sec^4 w$$
$$(\tan^2 w + 1)^2 \overset{?}{=} \sec^4 w$$
$$(\sec^2 w)^2 \overset{?}{=} \sec^4 w$$
$$\sec^4 w = \sec^4 w$$

4. $\sin^2 x(\csc^2 x + \sec^2 x) = \sec^2 x$

$$\sin^2 x(\csc^2 x + \sec^2 x) \overset{?}{=} \sec^2 x$$
$$1 + \dfrac{\sin^2 x}{\cos^2 x} \overset{?}{=} \sec^2 x$$
$$1 + \tan^2 x \overset{?}{=} \sec^2 x$$
$$\sec^2 x = \sec^2 x$$

5. $\dfrac{\sin x + \cos x}{1 - \sin x} = \dfrac{1 + \cot x}{\csc x - 1}$

$$\dfrac{\sin x + \cos x}{1 - \sin x} \overset{?}{=} \dfrac{1 + \cot x}{\csc x - 1}$$
$$\dfrac{\dfrac{\sin x}{\sin x} + \dfrac{\cos x}{\sin x}}{\dfrac{1}{\sin x} - \dfrac{\sin x}{\sin x}} \overset{?}{=} \dfrac{1 + \cot x}{\csc x - 1}$$
$$\dfrac{1 + \cot x}{\csc x - 1} = \dfrac{1 + \cot x}{\csc x - 1}$$

6. $\dfrac{1 - \tan x}{1 + \tan x} = \dfrac{\cot x - 1}{\cot x + 1}$

$$\dfrac{1 - \tan x}{1 + \tan x} \overset{?}{=} \dfrac{\cot x - 1}{\cot x + 1}$$
$$\dfrac{\dfrac{1}{\tan x} - \dfrac{\tan x}{\tan x}}{\dfrac{1}{\tan x} + \dfrac{\tan x}{\tan x}} \overset{?}{=} \dfrac{\cot x - 1}{\cot x + 1}$$
$$\dfrac{\cot x - 1}{\cot x + 1} = \dfrac{\cot x - 1}{\cot x + 1}$$

Algebra 2

NAME_____ DATE _____

Practice

Sum and Difference of Angles Formula

Find the exact value of each expression.

1. $\cos 75°$

2. $\cos 375°$

3. $\sin(-165°)$

4. $\sin(-105°)$

5. $\sin 95° \cos 55° + \cos 95° \sin 55°$

6. $\cos 160° \cos 40° + \sin 160° \sin 40°$

7. $\tan(135° + 120°)$

8. $\tan(315° - \theta)$

Verify that each of the following is an identity.

9. $\cos(180° - \theta) = -\cos \theta$

10. $\sin(360° + \theta) = \sin \theta$

11. $\sin(45° + \theta) - \sin(45° - \theta) = \sqrt{2} \sin \theta$

12. $\cos\left(x - \dfrac{\pi}{6}\right) + \sin\left(x - \dfrac{\pi}{3}\right) = \sin x$

Sum and Difference of Angles Formula

Find the exact value of each expression.

1. $\cos 75°$ $\dfrac{\sqrt{6} - \sqrt{2}}{4}$

2. $\cos 375°$ $\dfrac{\sqrt{6} + \sqrt{2}}{4}$

3. $\sin(-165°)$ $\dfrac{\sqrt{2} - \sqrt{6}}{4}$

4. $\sin(-105°)$ $\dfrac{-\sqrt{2} - \sqrt{6}}{4}$

5. $\sin 95° \cos 55° + \cos 95° \sin 55°$ $\dfrac{1}{2}$

6. $\cos 160° \cos 40° + \sin 160° \sin 40°$ $-\dfrac{1}{2}$

7. $\tan(135° + 120°)$ $2 + \sqrt{3}$

8. $\tan(315° - \theta)$ $\dfrac{\tan \theta + 1}{\tan \theta - 1}$

Verify that each of the following is an identity.

9. $\cos(180° - \theta) = -\cos \theta$
$\cos(180° - \theta)$
$= \cos 180° \cos \theta + \sin 180° \sin \theta$
$= (-1) \cos \theta + 0 \cdot \sin \theta$
$= -\cos \theta$

10. $\sin(360° + \theta) = \sin \theta$
$\sin(360° + \theta)$
$= \sin 360° \cos \theta + \cos 360° \sin \theta$
$= 0 \cdot \cos \theta + 1 \cdot \sin \theta$
$= \sin \theta$

11. $\sin(45° + \theta) - \sin(45° - \theta) = \sqrt{2} \sin \theta$
$\sin(45° + \theta) - \sin(45° - \theta)$
$= \sin 45° \cos \theta + \cos 45° \sin \theta -$
$\quad (\sin 45° \cos \theta - \cos 45° \sin \theta)$
$= 2 \cdot \cos 45° \sin \theta$
$= \sqrt{2} \sin \theta$

12. $\cos\left(x - \dfrac{\pi}{6}\right) + \sin\left(x - \dfrac{\pi}{3}\right) = \sin x$
$\cos\left(x - \dfrac{\pi}{6}\right) + \sin\left(x - \dfrac{\pi}{3}\right)$
$= \cos x \cos \dfrac{\pi}{6} + \sin x \sin \dfrac{\pi}{6} +$
$\quad \sin x \cos \dfrac{\pi}{3} - \cos x \sin \dfrac{\pi}{3}$
$= \dfrac{\sqrt{3}}{2} \cos x + \dfrac{1}{2} \sin x + \dfrac{1}{2} \sin x -$
$\quad \dfrac{\sqrt{3}}{2} \cos x$
$= \sin x$

Practice

Double-Angle and Half-Angle Formulas

Find the exact values of sin 2x, cos 2x, sin $\frac{x}{2}$, and cos $\frac{x}{2}$ for each of the following.

1. $\cos x = \frac{5}{13}$, x is in the first quadrant.

2. $\cos x = \frac{3}{7}$, x is in the fourth quadrant.

3. $\sin x = \frac{40}{41}$, x is in the second quadrant.

4. $\sin x = -\frac{4}{5}$, x is in the third quadrant.

5. $\sin x = -\frac{7}{8}$, x is in the third quadrant.

6. $\sin x = \frac{9}{10}$, x is in the second quadrant.

Find the exact value of each expression using the half-angle formulas.

7. $\tan 105°$

8. $\tan 15°$

9. $\cos 67\frac{1}{2}°$

10. $1 - 2 \sin^2 15°$

11. $8 \sin (22.5°) \cos (22.5°)$

12. $\sin \left(-\frac{\pi}{8}\right)$

Verify that each of the following is an identity.

13. $\sin 2\theta = \dfrac{2 \tan \theta}{1 + \tan^2 \theta}$

14. $\tan x + \cot x = 2 \csc 2x$

15. $\sin^2 \dfrac{x}{2} = \dfrac{\tan x - \sin x}{2 \tan x}$

16. $\sin 4\beta = 4 \cos 2\beta \sin \beta \cos \beta$

Practice

Double-Angle and Half-Angle Formulas

Find the exact values of $\sin 2x$, $\cos 2x$, $\sin \frac{x}{2}$, and $\cos \frac{x}{2}$ for each of the following.

1. $\cos x = \frac{5}{13}$, x is in the first quadrant.

$$\frac{120}{169}, \ -\frac{119}{169}, \ \frac{2\sqrt{13}}{13}, \ \frac{3\sqrt{13}}{13}$$

2. $\cos x = \frac{3}{7}$, x is in the fourth quadrant.

$$-\frac{12\sqrt{10}}{49}, \ -\frac{31}{49}, \ \frac{\sqrt{14}}{7}, \ -\frac{\sqrt{35}}{7}$$

3. $\sin x = \frac{40}{41}$, x is in the second quadrant.

$$-\frac{720}{1681}, \ -\frac{1519}{1681}, \ \frac{5\sqrt{41}}{41}, \ \frac{4\sqrt{41}}{41}$$

4. $\sin x = -\frac{4}{5}$, x is in the third quadrant.

$$\frac{24}{25}, \ -\frac{7}{25}, \ \frac{2\sqrt{5}}{5}, \ \frac{-\sqrt{5}}{5}$$

5. $\sin x = -\frac{7}{8}$, x is in the third quadrant.

$$\frac{7\sqrt{15}}{32}, \ -\frac{17}{32}, \ \frac{\sqrt{8+\sqrt{15}}}{4}, \ \frac{-\sqrt{8-\sqrt{15}}}{4}$$

6. $\sin x = \frac{9}{10}$, x is in the second quadrant.

$$-\frac{9\sqrt{19}}{50}, \ -\frac{31}{50}, \ \frac{\sqrt{50+5\sqrt{19}}}{10}, \ \frac{\sqrt{50-5\sqrt{19}}}{10}$$

Find the exact value of each expression using the half-angle formulas.

7. $\tan 105°$ $\quad -2 - \sqrt{3}$

8. $\tan 15°$ $\quad 2 - \sqrt{3}$

9. $\cos 67\frac{1}{2}°$ $\quad \dfrac{\sqrt{2-\sqrt{2}}}{2}$

10. $1 - 2\sin^2 15°$ $\quad \dfrac{\sqrt{3}}{2}$

11. $8 \sin (22.5°) \cos (22.5°)$ $\quad 2\sqrt{2}$

12. $\sin \left(-\dfrac{\pi}{8}\right)$ $\quad -\dfrac{\sqrt{2-\sqrt{2}}}{2}$

Verify that each of the following is an identity.

13. $\sin 2\theta = \dfrac{2\tan\theta}{1+\tan^2\theta}$

$$\sin 2\theta \overset{?}{=} \frac{2\tan\theta}{1+\tan^2\theta}$$

$$2\sin\theta\cos\theta \overset{?}{=} \frac{2\tan\theta}{\sec^2\theta}$$

$$2\sin\theta\cos\theta \overset{?}{=} \frac{2\sin\theta}{\cos\theta} \cdot \cos^2\theta$$

$$2\sin\theta\cos\theta = 2\sin\theta\cos\theta$$

14. $\tan x + \cot x = 2\csc 2x$

$$\tan x + \cot x \overset{?}{=} 2\csc 2x$$

$$\frac{\sin x}{\cos x} + \frac{\cos x}{\sin x} \overset{?}{=} \frac{2}{2\sin x\cos x}$$

$$\frac{\sin^2 x + \cos^2 x}{\cos x \sin x} \overset{?}{=} \frac{1}{\sin x\cos x}$$

$$\frac{1}{\cos x\sin x} = \frac{1}{\sin x\cos x}$$

15. $\sin^2 \dfrac{x}{2} = \dfrac{\tan x - \sin x}{2\tan x}$

$$\sin^2 \frac{x}{2} \overset{?}{=} \frac{\tan x - \sin x}{2\tan x}$$

$$\frac{1-\cos x}{2} \overset{?}{=} \frac{\dfrac{\tan x}{\tan x} - \dfrac{\sin x}{\tan x}}{2\dfrac{\tan x}{\tan x}}$$

$$\frac{1-\cos x}{2} = \frac{1-\cos x}{2}$$

16. $\sin 4\beta = 4\cos 2\beta \sin \beta \cos \beta$

$$\sin 4\beta \overset{?}{=} 4\cos 2\beta \sin\beta\cos\beta$$

$$\sin 2(2\beta) \overset{?}{=} 4\cos 2\beta \sin\beta\cos\beta$$

$$2\sin 2\beta\cos 2\beta \overset{?}{=} 4\cos 2\beta \sin\beta\cos\beta$$

$$2\cdot 2\sin\beta\cos\beta\cdot\cos 2\beta \overset{?}{=} 4\cos 2\beta \sin\beta\cos\beta$$

$$4\cos 2\beta\sin\beta\cos\beta = 4\cos 2\beta \sin\beta\cos\beta$$

NAME _____ DATE _____

Practice

Student Edition
Pages 861–867

Solving Trigonometric Equations

Find all solutions if $0° \leq x < 360°$.

1. $\sin 2x - \sqrt{3} \sin x = 0$

2. $\sqrt{2} \cos x = \sin 2x$

Find all solutions if $0 \leq x < 2\pi$.

3. $\cos x + \cos (90 - x) = 0$

4. $\tan^2 x + \sec x = 1$

Solve each equation for all values of x if x is measured in degrees.

5. $\sin^2 x \cos x = \cos x$

6. $\csc^2 x - 3 \csc x + 2 = 0$

7. $\dfrac{3}{1 + \cos x} = 4(1 - \cos x)$

8. $\sqrt{2} \cos^3 x = \cos^2 x$

Solve each equation for all values of θ if θ is measured in radians.

9. $\cos^2 \theta = \sin^2 \theta$

10. $\cot \theta = \cot^3 \theta$

11. $\sqrt{2} \sin^3 \theta = \sin^2 \theta$

12. $\cos^2 \theta \sin \theta = \sin \theta$

Practice

Solving Trigonometric Equations

Find all solutions if $0° \le x < 360°$.

1. $\sin 2x - \sqrt{3} \sin x = 0$
$0°, 180°, 30°, 330°$

2. $\sqrt{2} \cos x = \sin 2x$
$90°, 270°, 45°, 135°$

Find all solutions if $0 \le x < 2\pi$.

3. $\cos x + \cos (90 - x) = 0$
$\dfrac{3}{4}\pi, \dfrac{7}{4}\pi$

4. $\tan^2 x + \sec x = 1$
$0, \dfrac{2}{3}\pi, \dfrac{4}{3}\pi$

Solve each equation for all values of x if x is measured in degrees.

5. $\sin^2 x \cos x = \cos x$
$90° + 180n°$

6. $\csc^2 x - 3 \csc x + 2 = 0$
$30° + 360n°, 90° + 360n°,$
$150° + 360n°$

7. $\dfrac{3}{1 + \cos x} = 4(1 - \cos x)$
$60° + 180n°, 120° + 180n°$

8. $\sqrt{2} \cos^3 x = \cos^2 x$
$90° + 180n°, \pm 45° + 360n°$

Solve each equation for all values of θ if θ is measured in radians.

9. $\cos^2 \theta = \sin^2 \theta$
$\dfrac{\pi}{4} + \dfrac{\pi n}{2}$

10. $\cot \theta = \cot^3 \theta$
$\dfrac{\pi}{2} + n\pi, \dfrac{\pi}{4} + \dfrac{n\pi}{2}$

11. $\sqrt{2} \sin^3 \theta = \sin^2 \theta$
$\dfrac{\pi}{4} + 2\pi n, \dfrac{3\pi}{4} + 2\pi n$

12. $\cos^2 \theta \sin \theta = \sin \theta$
$0 + n\pi$